KS3
Success
Workbook

English
SATs

Levels 4-7

Kath Jordan

Contents

Reading fiction

Reading poetry

Reading non-fiction

Reading media texts

Writing

Shakespeare

Spelling, punctuation and grammar

SATS exam practice

Homework diary

TOPIC	STUDY DATE	SCORE
Post-1914 fiction		/22
Pre-1914 fiction		/22
Comparing texts		/22
'Death of a Naturalist'		/22
'Blackberry Picking'		/22
Comparing poems		/22
Autobiography/recount		/22
Information and explanation		/22
Persuasion and argument		/22
Media texts		/22
Writing to describe		/25
Writing to imagine, explore, entertain		/35
Writing to argue and persuade		/35
Writing to inform and explain		/25
Writing to review, analyse, comment		/25
Much Ado About Nothing		/22
Richard III		/22
The Tempest		/22
Spelling		/32
Punctuation and grammar		/32

How each topic will help you prepare for your exams

The Reading topics

The reading topics will help you prepare for the reading paper of your SATs. In the exam you will be given a reading booklet containing three texts or extracts. The texts included will be a combination of fiction, non-fiction, poetry and media. There will be 15 questions to answer.

The Writing topics

The writing topics will help you to prepare for the writing paper of your SATs. In the exam you will be required to complete two tasks that test your skills in two different writing triplets. One task should take 30 minutes and is worth 20 marks and the other task should take 45 minutes and is worth 30 marks. In this book some practice questions are worth 20 marks and some are worth 30 marks – check carefully before you begin.

The Shakespeare topics

The Shakespeare topics will help you to prepare for the Shakespeare paper of your SATs. In the exam you will be given a reading booklet containing two extracts from the Shakespeare play you have studied. There will be one question to answer.

The Spelling, Punctuation and Grammar topics

The spelling, punctuation and grammar topics will help you to prepare for all of your exam papers. Marks will be awarded for sentence structure, text organisation and spelling in the writing paper. Accurate spelling, punctuation and grammar will make your answers clearer in all of the exam papers.

The Spelling, Punctuation and Grammar topics

The SATs exam practice papers at the back of this book give more information about how marks will be awarded.

Post-1914 fiction

Read the extract carefully and answer the questions that follow.

In this extract Kingshaw, the young boy, has gone for a walk to escape the bully he and his mother are staying with. In the isolated cornfields some way from the house, he has a terrifying experience when he is chased by an unexpected predator.

When he first saw the crow he took no notice. There had been several crows. This one glided into the corn on its enormous, ragged black wings. He began to be aware of it when it rose up suddenly, circled overhead, and then dived, to land not very far away from him. Kingshaw could see the feathers on its head, shining black in between the butter-coloured cornstalks. Then it rose, and circled, and came down again, this time not quite landing, but flapping about his head, beating its wings and making a sound like flat leather pieces being slapped together. It was the largest crow he had ever seen. As it came down for the third time, he looked up and noticed its beak, opening in a screech. The inside of its mouth was scarlet, it had small glinting eyes.

Kingshaw got up and flapped his arms. For a moment, the bird retreated a little way off, and higher up in the sky. He began to walk rather quickly back, through the path in the corn, looking ahead of him. Stupid to be scared of a rotten bird. What could a bird do? But he felt his own extreme isolation, high up in the cornfield.

For a moment, he could only hear the soft thudding of his own footsteps, and the silky sound of the corn, brushing against him. Then there was a rush of air, as the great crow came beating down, and wheeled about his head. The beak opened and the hoarse caw came out again and again, from inside the scarlet mouth.

Kingshaw began to run, not caring now, if he trampled the corn, wanting to get away, down into the next field. He thought that the corn might be some kind of crow's food store, in which he was seen as an invader. Perhaps this was only the first of a whole battalion of crows, that would rise up and swoop at him. Get on the grass then, he thought, get on to the grass, that'll be safe, it'll go away. He wondered if it had mistaken him for some hostile animal, lurking down in the corn.

His progress was very slow, through the cornfield, the thick stalks bunched together and got in his way, and he had to shove them back with his arms. But he reached the gate and climbed it, and dropped on to the grass of the field on the other side. Sweat was running down his forehead and into his eyes. He looked up. The crow kept on coming. He ran.

But it wasn't easy to run down this field, either, because of the tractor ruts. He began

to leap wildly from side to side of them, his legs stretched as far as they could go, and for a short time, it seemed that he did go faster. The crow dived again, and, as it rose, Kingshaw felt the tip of its black wing, beating against his face. He gave a sudden, dry sob. Then his left foot caught in one of the ruts and he keeled over, going down straight forwards.

He lay with his face in the coarse grass, panting and sobbing by turns, with the sound of his own blood pumping through his ears. He felt the sun on the back of his neck, and his ankle was wrenched. But he would be able to get up. He raised his head, and wiped two fingers across his face. A streak of blood came off, from where a thistle had scratched him. He got unsteadily to his feet, taking in deep, desperate breaths of the close air. He could not see the crow.

But when he began to walk forwards again, it rose up from the grass a little way off, and began to circle and swoop. Kingshaw broke into a run, sobbing and wiping the damp mess of tears and sweat off his face with one hand. There was a blister on his ankle, rubbed raw by the sandal strap. The crow was still quite high, soaring easily, to keep pace with him. Now, he had scrambled over the third gate, and he was in the field next to the one that belonged to Warings. He could see the back of the house, he began to run much faster.

This time, he fell and lay completely winded. Through the runnels of sweat and the sticky tufts of his own hair, he could see a figure looking down at him from one of the top windows of the house.

Then, there was a single screech, and the terrible beating of wings, and the crow swooped down and landed in the middle of his back.

Kingshaw thought that, in the end, it must have been his screaming that frightened it off, for he dared not move. He lay and closed his eyes and felt the claws of the bird, digging into his skin, through the thin shirt, and began to scream in a queer, gasping sort of way. After a moment or two, the bird rose. He had expected it to begin pecking at him with its beak, remembering terrible stories about vultures that went for living people's eyes. He could not believe in his own escape.

From *I'm the King of the Castle*
by Susan Hill

Post-1914 fiction: questions

A

Choose just one answer, a, b, c or d.

1 Kingshaw is frightened because (1 mark)

a) he is lost in a cornfield ☐

b) he is lost in a forest ☐

c) he is being chased by a vulture ☐

d) he is being chased by a crow ☑

2 '... a sound like flat pieces of leather being slapped together' is (1 mark)

a) a metaphor ☐

b) a simile ☑

c) personification ☐

d) onomatopoeia ☐

3 Kingshaw found it difficult to run in the cornfield because (1 mark)

a) the cornstalks got in the way ☐

b) it was very muddy ☐

c) he had sprained his ankle ☐

d) the tractor ruts were too deep ☑

4 The bird hurt Kingshaw by (1 mark)

a) landing on his head ☑

b) pecking at his eyes ☐

c) digging its claws in his back ☐

d) knocking him to the ground ☐

5 Kingshaw escaped because (1 mark)

a) he ran away ☑

b) the bird flew away ☐

c) he chased the bird away ☐

d) his friend saved him ☐

Score / 5

B

Answer all parts of all questions.

1 Look at the section 'Kingshaw got up and flapped his arms' to 'lurking down in the corn'.

From this section, how do we know what Kingshaw is feeling?

Give two examples of what he thinks or does and explain how this shows what he is feeling. (4 marks)

Example: He wants to be a bird

Explanation: This is because he wants to a bird too run away

Example: Slapped the bird

Explanation: To hit the bird to shoe the bird

2 Look at the paragraph beginning 'His progress was very slow'.

a) What do you notice about the sentences at the end of this paragraph? (1 mark)

There is a short sentence.

b) What is the effect of this? (2 marks)

In/create suspence

Score / 7

C

This is a SATs-style question. Your answer should respond to each of the bullet points.

1 **How does the writer of this passage build increasing tension through this text?**

You should write about:

- the setting
- the structure of the text
- the way the character reacts to his situation. (10 marks)

The character reacts by running away from the crow. This means he wanted to get away. In addition, he did not like what the bird was doing.

The setting was emerald green field full of birds. Also mostly full of grass and hills.

Score **/ 10**

Total score **/ 22**

How well did you do? ✗ 0–6 **Try again** 7–10 **Getting there** 11–14 **Good work** 15–22 **Excellent!** ✓

For more help on this topic see KS3 English Success Guide pages 10–15.

9

Pre-1914 fiction

Read the extract carefully and answer the questions that follow.

In this extract Mr Lockwood, the narrator, is visiting Wuthering Heights. Bad weather and heavy snowfall across the Yorkshire Moors prevent him from leaving for home. Heathcliff, the ill-tempered owner of Wuthering Heights, is reluctant to allow Lockwood to stay for the night but a servant takes pity on him and shows him upstairs. He finds a disused room with a large oak bed next to a window ledge and decides to sleep there. That night he is unable to sleep well as he is plagued by bad dreams and noises outside the window.

This text was written in the nineteenth century so you may find some of the language difficult and unfamiliar. A glossary is provided at the end of the extract to help you with some of the unfamiliar vocabulary.

This time, I remembered I was lying in the oak closet, and I heard distinctly the gusty wind, and the driving snow; I heard also, the fir-bough repeat its teasing sound, and ascribed it to the right cause: but it annoyed me so much, that I resolved to silence it, if possible; and, I thought, I rose and endeavoured to unhasp the casement. The hook was soldered into the staple: a circumstance observed by me when awake, but forgotten.

'I must stop it, nevertheless!' I muttered, knocking my knuckles through the glass, and stretching an arm out to seize the importunate branch: instead of which, my fingers closed on the fingers of a little, ice-cold hand!

The intense horror of nightmare came over me; I tried to draw back my arm, but the hand clung to it, and a most melancholy voice sobbed,

'Let me in – let me in!'

'Who are you?' I asked, struggling, meanwhile, to disengage myself.

'Catherine Linton,' it replied. 'I'm come home: I'd lost my way on the moor!'

As it spoke, I discerned, obscurely, a child's face looking through the window.

Terror made me cruel; and, finding it useless to attempt shaking the creature off, I pulled its wrist on to the broken pane, and rubbed it to and fro till blood ran down and soaked the bed-clothes: still it wailed, 'Let me in!' and maintained its tenacious grip, almost maddening me with fear.

'How can I?' I said at length. 'Let *me* go, if you want me to let you in!'

The fingers relaxed, I snatched mine through the hole, hurriedly piled the books up in a pyramid against it, and stopped my ears to exclude the lamentable prayer.

I seemed to keep them closed above a quarter of an hour, yet, the instant I listened again, there was the doleful cry moaning on!

'Begone!' I shouted, 'I'll never let you in, not if you beg for twenty years!'
'It's twenty years,' mourned the voice, 'twenty years, I've been a waif for twenty years!'

From *Wuthering Heights*
by Emily Brontë (1818–1848)

Glossary   Ascribed: put it down to
Unhasp: unhook
Casement: window
Importunate: persistent/annoying
Discerned, obscurely: saw but not clearly
Tenacious: stubborn/firm

'Begone!' I shouted, 'I'll never let you in, not if you beg for twenty years!'
'It's twenty years,' mourned the voice, 'twenty years, I've been a waif for twenty years!'

Pre-1914 fiction: questions

A

Choose just one answer, a, b, c or d.

1 **The sentence type most often used in the dialogue (conversation) is** (1 mark)

a) interrogative ☐

b) exclamatory ☐

c) directive (imperative) ☑

d) declarative ☐

2 **The narrative perspective in this text is** (1 mark)

a) 1st person ☑

b) 2nd person ☐

c) 3rd person ☐

d) omniscient ☐

3 **At first the narrator believes the noise that wakes him is** (1 mark)

a) a child ☐

b) a bad dream ☑

c) a tree branch tapping on the window ☐

d) a ghost ☑

4 **The words *he, she, it* are** (1 mark)

a) nouns ☐

b) verbs ☐

c) adverbs ☐

d) pronouns ☑

5 **Which of the following words is *not* a synonym (alternative) for *lamentable*?** (1 mark)

a) laudable ☐

b) sorrowful ☑

c) sad ☑

d) woeful ☐

Score / 5

B

Answer all parts of all questions.

1 **Look again at the section beginning '"Who are you?" I asked'.**

a) Which pronoun does the author use to write about Catherine Linton and which pronoun would you expect the author to use? (2 marks)

Pronoun used: Who

Pronoun expected: Suspense

b) What effect does the author's choice of pronoun have? (2 marks)

To use a question to make the reader who is it!

2 **How would you describe the atmosphere of this text?**
List four words or phrases that help to create this atmosphere.

Atmosphere: snow falling

(1 mark)

Words and phrases:

(2 marks)

Score / 7

C These are SATs-style questions. Your answers should respond to each of the bullet points.

1 **Does the narrator show any sympathy towards Catherine Linton?**

You should write about:

• the language he uses to describe her

• what he says to her

• the way he behaves.

(5 marks)

He described by pale because she
was in the snow and it was cold.

How does the author create a feeling of fear and horror in this passage?

You should write about:

• the way the setting is described

• the language used in the extract

• the way the narrator behaves.

(5 marks)

Score   / 10

Total score   / 22

How well did you do?   ✗   **0–6 Try again**   **7–10 Getting there**   **11–14 Good work**   **15–22 Excellent!** ✓

For more help on this topic see KS3 English Success Guide pages 10–15.

13

Comparing texts

Read the two extracts carefully and answer the questions that follow.

In this extract Mr Sugden, the PE teacher, punishes Billy for playing badly in a football match by making him take a cold shower. Mr Sugden uses his authority to bully and intimidate Billy, his pupil.

He undressed quickly, bending his pumps free of his heels and sliding them off without untying the laces. When he stood up the black soles of his socks stamped damp imprints on the dry floor, which developed into a haphazard set of footprints when he removed his socks and stepped around pulling his jeans down. His ankles and knees were ingrained with ancient dirt which seemed to belong to the pigmentation of his skin. His left leg sported a mud stripe, and both his knees were encrusted. The surfaces of these mobile crusts were hair-lined, and with every flexion of the knee these lines opened into frown-like furrows.

For an instant, as he hurried into the showers, with one leg angled in running, with his dirty legs and huge rib cage moulding the skin of his white body, with his hollow cheek in profile, and the sabre of shadow emanating from the eye-hole, just for a moment he resembled an old print of a child hurrying towards the final solution.

* * *

While he worked on his ankles and heels Sugden stationed three boys at one end of the showers and moved to the other end, where the controls fed into the pipes on the wall . . . The blunt arrow was pointing to HOT. Sugden swung it back over WARM to COLD. For a few seconds there was no visible change in the temperature, and the red slice held steady, still dominating the dial. Then it began to recede, slowly at first, then swiftly, its share of the face diminishing rapidly.

The cold water made Billy gasp. He held out his hands as though testing for rain, then ran for the end. The three guards barred the exit.

'Hey up, shift! Let me out, you rotten dogs!' They held him easily so he swished back to the other end, yelling all the way along. Sugden pushed him in the chest as he clung his way round the corner.

'Got a sweat on, Casper?'

'Let me out, Sir. Let me come.'

'I thought you'd like a cooler after your exertions in goal.'

'I'm frozen!'

'Really?'

'Gi' o'er, Sir! It's not right!'

'And was it right when you let the last goal in?'

'I couldn't help it!'

'Rubbish, lad.'

Billy tried another rush. Sugden repelled it, so he tried the other end again. Every time he tried to escape the three boys bounced him back, stinging him with their snapping towels as he retreated. He tried manoeuvring the nozzles, but whichever way he twisted them the water still found him out. Until finally he gave up, and stood amongst them, tolerating the freezing spray in silence.

From *A Kestrel for a Knave*
by Barry Hines

14

Glossary Final solution: in World War II, Hitler's 'final solution' was to kill millions of Jews. Many of them were killed by gassing in mass showers.

In this extract George and Lennie meet Curley, the boss's son, for the first time. Curley uses his physical presence and aggression to intimidate Lennie.

His eyes passed over the new men and he stopped. He glanced coldly at George and then at Lennie. His arms gradually bent at the elbows and his hands closed into fists. He stiffened and went into a slight crouch. His glance was at once calculating and pugnacious. Lennie squirmed under the look and shifted his feet nervously. Curley stepped gingerly close to him. 'You the new guys the old man was waitin' for?'

'We just come,' said George.

'Let the big guy talk.'

Lennie twisted with embarrassment.

George said: 'S'pose he don't want to talk?'

Curley lashed his body around. 'By Christ, he's gotta talk when he's spoke to. What the hell are you gettin' into it for?'

'We travel together,' said George coldly.

'Oh, so it's that way.'

George was tense and motionless. 'Yeah, it's that way.'

Lennie was looking helplessly to George for instruction.

'An' you won't let the big guy talk, is that it?'

'He can talk if he wants to tell you anything.' He nodded slightly to Lennie.

'We jus' come in,' said Lennie softly.

Curley stared levelly at him. 'Well, nex' time you answer when you're spoke to.' He turned towards the door and walked out, and his elbows were still bent out a little.

George watched him out, and then turned back to the swamper. 'Say what the hell's he got on his shoulder? Lennie didn't do nothing to him.'

The old man looked cautiously at the door to make sure no one was listening. 'That's the boss's son,' he said quietly. 'Curley's pretty handy. He's done quite a bit in the ring. He's a lightweight, and he's handy.'

'Well let him be handy,' said George. 'He don't have to take after Lennie. Lennie didn't do nothing to him. What's he got against Lennie?'

The swamper considered: '– Well – tell you what. Curley's like a lot of little guys. He hates big guys. He's alla time picking scraps with big guys. Kind of like he's mad at 'em because he ain't a big guy. You seen little guys like that, ain't you? Always scrappy?'

'Sure,' said George. 'I seen plenty tough little guys. But this Curley better not make no mistakes about Lennie. Lennie ain't handy, but this Curley punk is gonna get hurt if he messes around with Lennie.'

From *Of Mice and Men*
by John Steinbeck

Comparing texts: questions

A

Choose just one answer, a, b, c or d.

1 **Mr Sugden was angry with Billy because** (1 mark)

a) he let a goal in ☐

b) he refused to have a shower ☐

c) he bullied another pupil ☐

d) he wouldn't join in the PE lesson ☐

2 **Another verb that means _tolerate_ is** (1 mark)

a) enjoy ☐

b) endure ☐

c) refuse ☐

d) fight ☐

3 **Which punctuation mark is used most in the speech of Billy and Mr Sugden?** (1 mark)

a) comma ☐

b) question mark ☐

c) full stop ☐

d) exclamation mark ☐

4 **Which verb is _not_ used to describe Lennie's movement?** (1 mark)

a) squirmed ☐

b) shifted ☐

c) shuffled ☐

d) twisted ☐

5 **In the second extract the reader's sympathy is with** (1 mark)

a) Curley ☐

b) Lennie ☐

c) George ☐

d) the swamper ☐

Score / 5

B

Answer all parts of all questions.

1 Look closely at the way the dialogue is punctuated in the first extract.
Give the two main punctuation marks used and explain what effect this has.

Punctuation: .... (1 mark)

Explanation: .... (1 mark)

2 Look closely at the section beginning 'For an instant' (_A Kestrel for a Knave_).
Explain how this comparison creates sympathy for Billy. (2 marks)

....

....

....

3 Look closely at the section beginning 'His eyes passed over the new men' and ending
'What the hell are you gettin' into it for?' (_Of Mice and Men_).

Give two words or phrases used to make Curley seem threatening and explain why they are effective.

Words and phrases: .... (1 mark)

Explanation: .... (2 marks)

Score / 7

C

This is a SATs-style question. Your answer should respond to each of the bullet points.

1 **Compare the ways in which the two writers create sympathy for the victims of bullying and intimidation.**

You should write about:

• the way Billy and Lennie react to their situations

• the way the bullies are presented

• the way that other characters behave towards and talk about the main characters.   **(10 marks)**

....

....

....

....

....

....

....

....

....

....

....

....

....

....

....

....

....

....

....

....

....

....

....

Score   / 10

Total score   / 22

How well did you do?   ✗ 0–6 **Try again**   7–10 **Getting there**   11–14 **Good work**   15–22 **Excellent!** ✓

For more help on this topic see KS3 English Success Guide pages 10–15.

Death of a Naturalist

Read both poems carefully and answer the questions that follow. Questions on pages 24–25 require you to compare the two poems.

Death of a Naturalist

All year the flax-dam festered in the heart
Of the townland; green and heavy headed
Flax had rotted there, weighted down by huge sods.
Daily it sweltered in the punishing sun.
Bubbles gargled delicately, bluebottles
Wove a strong gauze of sound around the smell.
There were dragon-flies, spotted butterflies,
But best of all was the warm thick slobber
Of frogspawn that grew like clotted water
In the shade of the banks. Here, every spring
I would fill jampotsful of the jellied
Specks to range on window-sills at home,
On shelves at school, and wait and watch until
The fattening dots burst into nimble-
Swimming tadpoles. Miss Walls would tell us how
The daddy frog was called a bullfrog
And how he croaked and how the mammy frog
Laid hundreds of little eggs and this was
Frogspawn. You could tell the weather by frogs too
For they were yellow in the sun and brown
In rain.

Then one hot day when fields were rank
With cowdung in the grass and angry frogs
Invaded the flax-dam; I ducked through hedges
To a coarse croaking that I had not heard
Before. The air was thick with a bass chorus.
Right down the dam gross-bellied frogs were cocked
On sods; their loose necks pulsed like sails. Some hopped:
The slap and plop were obscene threats. Some sat
Poised like mud grenades, their blunt heads farting.
I sickened, turned, and ran. The great slime kings
Were gathered there for vengeance and I knew
That if I dipped my hand the spawn would clutch it.

Seamus Heaney

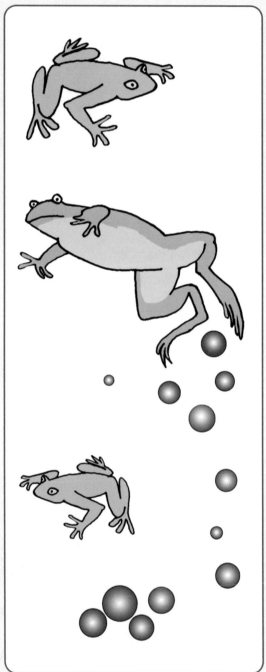

Blackberry Picking

Blackberry Picking

Late August, given heavy rain and sun
For a full week, the blackberries would ripen.
At first, just one, a glossy purple clot
Among others, red, green, hard as a knot.
You ate the first one and its flesh was sweet
Like thickened wine: summer's blood was in it
Leaving stains upon the tongue and lust for
Picking. Then red ones inked up and that hunger
Sent us out with milk-cans, pea-tins, jam-pots
Where briars scratched and wet grass bleached our boots.
Round hayfields, cornfields and potato-drills
We trekked and picked until the cans were full,
Until the tinkling bottom had been covered
With green ones, and on top big dark blobs burned
Like a plate of eyes. Our hands were peppered
With thorn pricks, our palms sticky as Bluebeard's.

We hoarded the fresh berries in the byre.
But when the bath was filled we found a fur,
A rat grey fungus, glutting on our cache.
The juice was stinking too. Once off the bush
The fruit fermented, the sweet flesh would turn sour.
I always felt like crying. It wasn't fair
That all the lovely canfuls smelt of rot.
Each year I hoped they would keep, knew they would not.

Seamus Heaney

Glossary   Bluebeard: a pirate who killed many of his wives by chopping off their heads.
Byre: a cowshed.
Cache: a hidden store of treasure, provisions or weapons.

Death of a Naturalist: questions

A

Choose just one answer, a, b, c or d.

1 The poem is called 'Death of a Naturalist' because (1 mark)

a) a naturalist is killed ☐

b) the boy kills the frogs ☐

c) the boy loses his interest in nature ☐

d) the 'great slime kings' kill the boy ☐

2 When does the boy collect frogspawn? (1 mark)

a) all year ☐

b) every day ☐

c) every spring ☐

d) every summer ☐

3 'Poised like mud grenades' is (1 mark)

a) a metaphor ☐

b) personification ☐

c) an oxymoron ☐

d) a simile ☐

4 Which of the following techniques is *not* used in the poem? (1 mark)

a) onomatopoeia ☐

b) simile ☐

c) rhyme ☐

d) alliteration ☐

5 How many different voices can you hear in the poem? (1 mark)

a) one ☐

b) two ☐

c) three ☐

d) four ☐

Score / 5

B

Answer all parts of all questions.

1 To organise his poem the poet uses references to time. Give two examples of references to time and explain why they are effective. (4 marks)

Example: ....

Explanation: ....

Example: ....

Explanation: ....

2 Look closely at the final sentence of the poem. Explain why the poet uses the phrase 'I knew'. (2 marks)

....

....

3 Put the events of the poem in order by numbering the following points. (1 mark)

.... The boy is frightened of the frogs and runs away.

.... The boy collects frogspawn every spring.

.... The boy describes his favourite place to collect frogspawn.

.... One day the boy hears an unfamiliar sound.

.... The boy recounts all the things he knows about frogs and frogspawn.

Score / 7

C These are SATs-style questions. Your answers should respond to each of the bullet points.

1 **Look closely at the sentence structure in the poem.**
How does the poet use sentence structure to reflect the feelings of the boy in the poem?

You should write about:

• the sentence beginning 'Here, every spring'

• the sentence beginning 'I sickened'

• the difference between the way the boy feels at the beginning of the poem and at the end. **(4 marks)**

....

....

....

....

....

....

....

....

How does the poet use sensory images to make the reader feel involved in the poem?

You should write about:

• specific images from the poem

• how the poet appeals to the reader's senses. **(6 marks)**

....

....

....

....

....

....

....

....

....

....

....

Score   / 10

Total score   / 22

How well did you do? ✗ 0–6 **Try again** 7–10 **Getting there** 11–14 **Good work** 15–22 **Excellent!** ✓

For more help on this topic see KS3 English Success Guide pages 18–23.

21

Blackberry Picking: questions

A

Choose just one answer, a, b, c or d.

1 Which of the following voices can you hear in the poem? (1 mark)

a) the adult poet only ☐

b) the adult poet and his mother ☐

c) the poet as a child only ☐

d) the adult poet and the poet as a child ☐

2 'summer's blood was in it' is (1 mark)

a) a simile ☐

b) personification ☐

c) onomatopoeia ☐

d) alliteration ☐

3 Which statement best describes the way rhyme is used in this poem? (1 mark)

a) there is no rhyme scheme ☐

b) the poem is written in rhyming couplets ☐

c) the poem uses half rhyme and complete end rhymes ☐

d) the poem has an 'abab' rhyme scheme ☐

4 As the berries ripen they change colour. Choose the correct order: (1 mark)

a) grey, green, purple, red ☐

b) green, red, purple, grey ☐

c) red, grey, purple, green ☐

d) purple, green, red, grey ☐

5 What happens to the berries at the end of the poem? (1 mark)

a) a rat eats them ☐

b) somebody steals them from the byre ☐

c) the fruit ferments and turns into wine ☐

d) they rot ☐

Score / 5

B

Answer all parts of all questions.

1 Write down two similes used in the first stanza and explain why each is effective. (4 marks)

Simile:...

Explanation: ....

....

....

Simile:...

Explanation: ....

....

....

2 Find two words in the second stanza which link to 'Bluebeard' in the first stanza. Explain why the poet has used the image these words help to create. (3 marks)

Words used: ....

Explanation: ....

....

....

Score / 7

C

These are SATs-style questions. Your answers should respond to each of the bullet points.

1 **The first stanza of the poem uses images connected to life and blood, e.g. 'purple clot'.**

Explain why these images are used and how they can be connected to Bluebeard.

You should write about:

• specific vocabulary and images

• the connection between life/blood, Bluebeard and what the boy is doing.   (5 marks)

....

....

....

....

....

....

....

....

....

2 **What techniques does the poet use to show how the child's emotions change from the first stanza to the second stanza of the poem?**

You should write about:

• vocabulary choices and imagery

• the way that movement is described

• sentence length and structure.   (5 marks)

....

....

....

....

....

....

....

....

....

....

....

Score   / 10

Total score   / 22

How well did you do?   ✗ 0–6 Try again   7–10 Getting there   11–14 Good work   15–22 Excellent! ✓

For more help on this topic see KS3 English Success Guide pages 18–23.

Comparing poems

A

Choose just one answer, a, b, c or d.

1 In both poems which answer best describes the emotions represented? **(1 mark)**

a) fear turns to excitement ☐

b) boredom turns to fear ☐

c) excitement turns to disappointment and fear ☐

d) curiosity turns to boredom ☐

2 Which type of imagery is used most in the two poems? **(1 mark)**

a) simile ☐

b) personification ☐

c) metaphor ☐

d) oxymoron ☐

3 Which answer best describes the main voice in the two poems? **(1 mark)**

a) adult writing about adult experience ☐

b) child writing about childhood experience ☐

c) child writing about adult experience ☐

d) adult writing about childhood experience ☐

4 The theme of the two poems is **(1 mark)**

a) being frightened of nature ☐

b) losing childhood innocence ☐

c) eating blackberries and catching frogspawn ☐

d) wishing to be young again ☐

5 What is the main difference in the structure of the two poems? **(1 mark)**

a) the number of stanzas ☐

b) sentence length ☐

c) use of enjambment ☐

d) rhyme ☐

Score **/ 5**

B

Answer all parts of all questions.

1 In both poems the poet uses a mixture of long and short sentences to represent different emotions. Write down the emotion(s) that each sentence type represents. **(2 marks)**

Long sentences:..

Short sentences:...

2 In both poems the poet uses images or vocabulary to describe childhood experience that a child wouldn't use. Give an example from each poem and explain what it adds to the poem. **(4 marks)**

Example:..

Explanation: ....

Example:..

Explanation: ....

3 Write down three similarities between the two poems. **(1 mark)**

a) ....

b) ....

c) ....

Score **/ 7**

C

This is a SATs-style question. Your answer should respond to each of the bullet points.

1 Compare the ways in which the poet recreates his memories of childhood in the poems 'Death of a Naturalist' and 'Blackberry Picking'.

You should write about:

• the way the setting and actions are described

• the emotions he felt

• the structure, imagery and vocabulary used in the poems.

(10 marks)

....

....

....

....

....

....

....

....

....

....

....

....

....

....

....

....

....

....

....

....

....

....

....

....

....

Score   / 10

Total score   / 22

How well did you do?   ✗ **0–6 Try again   7–10 Getting there   11–14 Good work   15–22 Excellent!** ✓

For more help on this topic see KS3 English Success Guide pages 18–23.

Read the extract carefully and answer the questions that follow.

This extract is from Nelson Mandela's autobiography *Long Walk to Freedom*. He writes about his rural African upbringing, his struggle against apartheid, his imprisonment and finally his election as President of South Africa. This extract is from the section entitled 'Robben Island: the dark years', in which he describes his prison life.

In the midst of breakfast, the guards would yell, 'Val in! Val in!' (Fall in! Fall in!), and we would stand outside our cells for inspection. Each prisoner was required to have the three buttons of his khaki jacket properly buttoned. We were required to doff our hats as the warder walked by. If our buttons were undone, our hats unremoved, or our cells untidy, we were charged with a violation of the prison code and punished with either solitary confinement or the loss of meals.

After inspection we would work in the courtyard hammering stones until noon. There were no breaks; if we slowed down the warders would yell at us to speed up. At noon, the bell would clang for lunch and another metal drum of food would be wheeled into the courtyard. For Africans, lunch consisted of boiled mealies, that is, coarse kernels of corn. The Indians and Coloured prisoners received samp, or mealie rice, which consisted of ground mealies in a soup-like mixture. The samp was sometimes served with vegetables, whereas our mealies were served straight.

For lunch we often received phuzamandla, which means 'drink of strength', a powder made from mealies and a bit of yeast. It is meant to be stirred into water or milk, and when it is thick it can be tasty, but the prison authorities gave us so little of the powder that it barely coloured the water. I would usually save my powder for several days until I had enough to make a proper drink, but if the authorities discovered you were hoarding food, the powder was confiscated and you were punished.

After lunch we worked until 4, when the guards blew shrill whistles and we once again lined up to be counted and inspected. We were then permitted half an hour to clean up. The bathroom at the end of our corridor had two seawater showers, a saltwater tap and three large galvanized metal buckets, which were used as bathtubs. There was no hot water. We would stand or squat in these buckets, soaping ourselves with the brackish water, rinsing off the dust from the day. To wash yourself with cold water when it is cold outside is not pleasant, but we made the best of it. We would sometimes sing while washing, which made the water seem less icy. In those early days, this was one of the only times when we could converse.

Precisely at 4.30 there would be a loud knock on the wooden door at the end of the corridor, which meant that supper had been delivered. Common-law prisoners used to dish out the food to us and we would return to our cells to eat it. We again received mealie pap porridge, sometimes with the odd carrot or piece of cabbage or beetroot thrown in – but one usually had to search for it. If we did get a vegetable, we would usually have the same one for weeks on end, until the cabbage or carrots were old and mouldy and we thoroughly sick of them. Every other day we received a small piece of meat with our porridge. The meat was mostly gristle.

For supper, Coloured and Indian prisoners received a quarter loaf of bread (known as katkopf that is, a cat's head, after the shape of the bread) and a slab of margarine. Africans, it was presumed, did not care for bread as it was a 'European' type of food.

Typically, we received even less than the scanty amounts stipulated in the regulations. This was because the kitchen was rife with smuggling. The cooks – all of whom were common-law prisoners – kept the best food for themselves or their friends. Often they would lay aside the tastiest morsel for the warders in exchange for favours or preferential treatment.

At 8 p.m. the night warder would lock himself in the corridor with us, passing the key through a small hole in the door to another warder outside. The warder would then walk up and down the corridor, ordering us to go to sleep. No cry of 'lights out' was ever given on Robben Island because the single mesh-covered bulb in our cell burned day and night. Later, those studying for higher degrees were permitted to read until 10 or 11 p.m.

From *Long Walk to Freedom*
by Nelson Mandela

A

Choose just one answer, a, b, c or d.

1 *Katkopf* means   (1 mark)

a) drink of strength ☐

b) fall in ☐

c) lights out ☐

d) cat's head ☐

2 Prisoners had to go to sleep at   (1 mark)

a) 7 p.m. ☐

b) 8 p.m. ☐

c) 10 p.m. ☐

d) 11 p.m. ☐

3 Which of the following is *not* a feature of a recount text?   (1 mark)

a) written in the present tense ☐

b) temporal (time) connectives ☐

c) events told in order ☐

d) focuses on specified individuals or groups ☐

4 When was inspection?   (1 mark)

a) before breakfast ☐

b) after breakfast ☐

c) during breakfast ☐

d) before lights out ☐

5 Africans didn't receive bread because   (1 mark)

a) they didn't like it ☐

b) the common-law prisoners stole it ☐

c) the prison authorities thought they didn't like 'European' food ☐

d) it was kept back as punishment ☐

Score   / 5

B

Answer all parts of all questions.

1 Which part of the prison routine is described in most detail? Explain what this detail emphasises. Find and copy a quotation to support your explanation.   (3 marks)

Part of routine: ....

Explanation: ....

....

Quotation: ....

2 This is a recount text. Find and copy an example of each of the following features of a recount.   (2 marks)

Temporal connective: ....

Focuses on individuals or identified groups: ....

....

3 This extract uses language from another country. Find an example and explain how the meaning has been made clear to the reader.   (2 marks)

Example:...

Explanation: ....

....

Score   / 7

C

This is a SATs-style question. Your answer should respond to each of the bullet points.

1 Explain how the writer highlights the harshness of the routine and the prejudice he encountered whilst in prison.

You should write about:

- the way he describes the daily routine
- what he does to cope with the routine
- his relationships with others
- punishments. (10 marks)

....
....
....
....
....
....
....
....
....
....
....
....
....
....
....

....
....
....
....
....
....
....

Score / 10

Total score / 22

How well did you do? ✗ 0–6 **Try again** 7–10 **Getting there** 11–14 **Good work** 15–22 **Excellent!** ✓

For more help on this topic see KS3 English Success Guide pages 26–33.

29

Digitising & Restoring
Tapes & Records on Your PC

A PC with a CD burner and soundcard provides the ideal means to preserve old tape recordings or transfer your vinyl collection to CD

Martin Walker

One of the reasons many PC users have for buying a soundcard is to transfer recordings from older analogue media such as vinyl or tape, and burn them to CD so that they can easily be listened to and archived. In this month's PC Musician I'm going to take you through the three stages of this process: getting the audio from your tape or record into the PC, carrying out any processing or restoration work that may be appropriate, and burning it to CD.

Preparing Your Material

The obvious thing to ensure first of all is that whatever analogue playback device you're using to get the audio into your computer, be it a reel-to-reel or cassette tape deck or a turntable, is set up to yield the best possible audio quality. If you're using a tape machine, for instance, make sure that the heads and mechanism are cleaned, and it's also worth cleaning vinyl records properly before you transfer them.

The output of tape decks can be directly connected to a suitable line-level input on your soundcard. Most cassette decks will have –10 dBV consumer output levels, while more professional reel-to-reel tape machines will need your soundcard's +4 dBU input sensitivity setting. If you're

transferring records, however, you'll need to amplify and correctly equalise the low output level from your record deck's magnetic cartridge before you can connect it to a soundcard. Typical signal levels are around 5 mV from an MM (moving magnet) pickup, and 0.5 mV from an MC (moving coil) pickup, so you should keep the deck well away from both your PC and its CRT monitor.

Many musicians will still have hi-fis with a suitable phono input, and some mixers provide them, but otherwise you'll need a preamp with the RIAA (Recording Industries Association of America) equalisation that provides a flat overall frequency response. Phono preamps are available as stand-alone boxes from various specialist hi-fi retailers, and in DIY form from companies like Maplin (www.maplin.co.uk) but soundcard manufacturers have also spotted this niche. Terratec, for instance, offer a stand-alone phono preamp that draws its power from the 15-pin Gameport

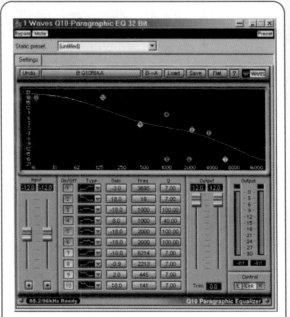

Here's a carefully tweaked RIAA de-emphasis curve that's provided by Waves in their collection of Q10 pre/De-Emphasis presets. Notice the 12dB on the input faders to prevent digital overload.

connector found on many consumer soundcards, while you can buy Steinberg's low-cost *Clean!* software (reviewed in *SOS* July 1999) bundled with an RIAA preamp for £79.99. Most phono preamps will probably have the lower –10 dBV output level.

If you don't have a dedicated RIAA-compatible preamp, you could try using a mic preamp and then an EQ plug-in to boost the bass end and roll off the treble end to compensate for the response of the cutting lathe. I've detailed some suitable settings in the RIAA Equalisation Using An EQ Plug-in box.

When it comes to actually playing back your tapes, it's important to get the right playback settings on your tape

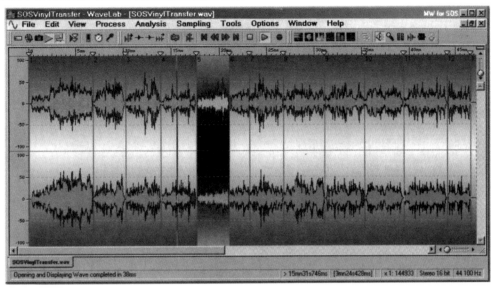

With a suitable editor like *Wavelab*, you can keep an entire album's worth of tracks in one file using suitable markers, and process them on a global or individual basis.

recorder. Obviously, you should set up cassette recorders appropriately for ferrochrome, chrome or metal tapes, while reel-to-reel recorders may give you a choice between IEC or NAB playback EQ (although this can be corrected once in the PC using a suitable EQ plug-in such as Waves' *Q10*). For most recordings, you'll also need to decide whether or not you need noise reduction enabled, and if so of which type – Dolby A, B or C, Dbx and so on. Nearly all prerecorded cassettes use Dolby B, but if you don't know what type was used on a particular recording, it's often possible to guess. If you hear background noise levels 'pumping' with noise reduction switched out, the chances are that the recording used noise reduction, and most likely Dolby B. If you don't know, choose the type that gives the most natural-sounding result compared with other known recordings.

Recording into a Soundcard

I can see little point in using a soundcard sample rate other than 44.1 kHz if you're transferring audio to be put on CD, while 16-bit recording should provide more than enough dynamic range to capture any analogue tape. However, vinyl freaks with pristine record collections may want to instead choose 88.2 kHz and 24-bit, to preserve the maximum amount of detail and high-frequency extension until the last possible moment. If you've got a consumer soundcard with loads of inputs like the Soundblaster Live! range, make sure you mute all but the one you're using, to minimise background noise levels.

It's best to experiment a little to find the optimum recording level, to make sure you get the maximum dynamic range onto the hard disk recording. Many PC audio recording applications and soundcard utilities provide an input meter with text readout of the highest recorded level, so start by running through a couple of tracks to see what this is, and then adjust the output level of your tape player or mixer accordingly, so that you still have one or two dBs of headroom left. For instance, if your peak meter reads –5 dB, you can safely increase input level by at least 3 dB without worrying about running into clipping. If you know the recordings well, you'll probably already know where the loudest parts are likely to be. You may well only have to do this once for a particular deck, and can then run through a whole batch of tapes or records with the same settings, so it's worth doing carefully.

Before you get stuck in, take a careful look at the recording facilities offered by your audio application, since there may be some real time-savers among them. For instance, *Wavelab* provides a selection of auto-start and auto-stop options that can automate the process of recording albums. I find its 'Auto-create markers at silence points' function particularly useful, since it places suitable CD track markers in gaps in the audio. Although you'll probably have to move their positions forward so that they coincide with the start of the next track rather than the fade out of the previous one, it's better than doing everything by hand.

Before you hit Record, check that you've got enough hard drive space. At 10 Mb per stereo minute at 44.1 kHz/16-bit, you'll need about 650 Mb per CD, and if you envisage doing any PC audio editing you'll need double this amount of space to store the temporary files. During vinyl transfers you should keep your monitor levels quiet: otherwise, acoustic feedback could modify the frequency response of the recording. For the same reason, avoid moving about during the recording if your floor isn't solid.

Sound on Sound
August 2002

Information and explanation: questions

A

Choose just one answer, a, b, c or d.

1 This article explains how to (1 mark)

a) make your own original recordings ☐

b) transfer tape and vinyl recordings to CD ☐

c) make music using your PC ☐

d) listen to music via the internet ☐

2 MM stands for (1 mark)

a) moving microphone ☐

b) moving magnet ☐

c) micro-magnet ☐

d) music magnet ☐

3 Audio means (1 mark)

a) music ☐

b) speech ☐

c) sound ☐

d) recording ☐

4 Most pre-recorded cassettes use (1 mark)

a) Dolby A ☐

b) Dolby B ☐

c) Dolby C ☐

d) Dolby D ☐

5 How much hard drive space do you need to record a CD on your PC? (1 mark)

a) 10 Mb ☐

b) 1300 Mb ☐

c) 44.1 kHz ☐

d) 650 Mb ☐

Score / 5

B

Answer all parts of all questions.

1 Give two ways you can tell this article is aimed at a specialist audience. (2 marks)

....

....

2 This article sets out to explain a three-stage process. In your own words, briefly explain what the three stages are. (3 marks)

a) ....

b) ....

c) ....

3 This article uses logical and temporal (sequence) connectives. Find and copy an example of each. (1 mark)

Logical connective: ....

Temporal connective: ....

4 Look at the paragraph beginning 'If you don't have a dedicated'.
Find and copy the (modal auxiliary) verb which indicates that advice is being given. (1 mark)

....

....

Score / 7

C

This is a SATs-style question. Your answer should respond to each of the bullet points.

1 **Comment on the effectiveness of the language and layout in this article.**

You should write about:

• the intended purpose and audience of the article

• use of technical, formal and informal language

• the use of pictures, headings and subheadings

• overall organisation. (10 marks)

....

....

....

....

....

....

....

....

....

....

....

....

....

....

....

....

....

....

....

....

....

....

....

....

....

....

Score **/ 10**

Total score **/ 22**

How well did you do? ✗ 0–6 **Try again** 7–10 **Getting there** 11–14 **Good work** 15–22 **Excellent!** ✓

For more help on this topic see KS3 English Success Guide pages 26–27.

Persuasion and argument

The extract printed below is the final part of a speech delivered by the Reverend Martin Luther King at a civil rights march in Washington (28 August 1963).

I have a dream . . .

So I say to you, my friends, that even though we must face the difficulties of today and tomorrow, I still have a dream. It is a dream deeply rooted in the American dream that one day this nation will rise up and live out the true meaning of its creed – we hold these truths to be self-evident, that all men are created equal.

I have a dream that one day on the red hills of Georgia, sons of former slaves and sons of former slave-owners will be able to sit down together at the table of brotherhood.

I have a dream that one day, even the state of Mississippi, a state sweltering with the heat of injustice, sweltering with the heat of oppression, will be transformed into an oasis of freedom and justice.

I have a dream that my four little children will one day live in a nation where they will not be judged by the colour of their skin but by the content of their character. I have a dream today!

I have a dream that one day, down in Alabama, with its vicious racists, with its governor having his lips dripping with the words of interposition and nullification, that one day, right there in Alabama, little black boys and black girls will be able to join hands with little white boys and white girls as sisters and brothers. I have a dream today!

I have a dream that one day every valley shall be exalted, every hill and mountain shall be made low, the rough places shall be made plain, and the crooked places shall be made straight and the glory of the Lord will be revealed and all flesh shall see it together.

This is our hope. This is the faith that I go back to the South with.

With this faith we will be able to bear out of the mountain of despair a stone of hope. With this faith we will be able to transform the jangling discord of our nation into a beautiful symphony of brotherhood.

With this faith we will be able to work together, to pray together, to struggle together, to go to jail together, to stand up for freedom together; knowing that we will be free one day. This will be the day when all of God's children will be able to sing with new meaning – 'my country 'tis of thee; sweet land of liberty, land where my fathers died, land of the pilgrim's pride; from every mountain side, let freedom ring' – and if America is to be a great nation, this must become true.

So let freedom ring from the prodigious hilltops of New Hampshire.

Let freedom ring from the mighty mountains of New York.

Let freedom ring from the heightening Alleghenies of Pennsylvania.

Let freedom ring from the snow-capped Rockies of Colorado.

Let freedom ring from the curvaceous slopes of California.

But not only that.

Let freedom ring from Stone Mountain of Georgia.

Let freedom ring from Lookout Mountain of Tennessee.

Let freedom ring from every hill and molehill of Mississippi, from every mountain side, let freedom ring.

When we let freedom ring, when we let it ring from every village and every hamlet, from every state and every city, we will be able to speed up that day when all of God's children, black men and white men, Jews and Gentiles, Protestants and Catholics, will be able to join hands and sing in the words of the old Negro spiritual, 'Free at last! free at last! thank God Almighty, we are free at last!'

The writer of the following passage argues that watching television can be bad for your health.

Too much television can damage your child's health

Television may be part of everyday life for most children but is it safe? In our hectic lives we are so busy managing our private and professional concerns and relationships, we allow our children to spend a huge percentage of their unsupervised time watching television. So busy, in fact, that most of us don't stop to consider the hidden dangers of unlimited viewing.

The health risks which attend excessive television viewing are extensive and, to my mind, should not be underestimated. It contributes to the growing problems of adolescent obesity; it prevents regular exercise which could cause heart problems in later life; it causes psychological problems if children are exposed to inappropriate materials and it can damage eyesight.

However, the most worrying problem is the detrimental effect that too much television can have on the early stages of a child's development. Playing games, listening to stories and interacting with other children are all essential to a child's emotional, physical and communicational development. When television takes the place of these activities, we allow untold damage to be done.

Of course, many would be quick to defend the educational value of television and there is no doubt that properly managed television viewing can be beneficial. In my opinion, however, the dangers far outweigh the benefits. Until parents make time to exercise proper control over their children's viewing habits, children's health will continue to suffer.

Persuasion and argument: questions

A

Choose just one answer, a, b, c or d.

1 The persuasive technique used most in Martin Luther King's speech is *(1 mark)*

a) rhetorical question ☐

b) emotive language ☐

c) repetition ☐

d) short exclamatory sentences ☐

2 Which of the following pronouns are used most in the speech? *(1 mark)*

a) he and she ☐

b) I and we ☐

c) you and it ☐

d) us and them ☐

3 The intended audience of 'Too much television' is *(1 mark)*

a) health professionals ☐

b) teachers ☐

c) children ☐

d) adults – particularly parents ☐

4 The sentence type used most in 'Too much television' is *(1 mark)*

a) simple ☐

b) complex ☐

c) compound ☐

d) interrogative ☐

5 The title 'Too much television can damage your child's health' is *(1 mark)*

a) a fact ☐

b) an opinion ☐

c) an opinion presented as fact ☐

d) a fact presented as opinion ☐

Score   / 5

B

Answer all parts of all questions.

These questions all relate to 'Too much television can damage your child's health'.

1 Find and copy two connective words or phrases used in the passage. *(1 mark)*

a) ....

b) ....

2 What type of question is used in the first sentence? Explain the effect of opening the text in this way. *(2 marks)*

Question type: ....

Explanation: ....

3 Give two examples of problems caused by too much television viewing and explain why these problems occur. *(4 marks)*

Example:..

Explanation: ....

....

Example:..

Explanation: ....

....

Score   / 7

C

These are SATs-style questions. Your second answer should respond to each of the bullet points.

These questions all relate to 'I have a dream'.

1 Give two examples of words, phrases or themes that are repeated in the speech and explain how each is used to add emphasis. (4 marks)

Example:...

Explanation: ....

Example:...

Explanation: ....

How does the writer use sentence structure to control the pace and emphasis of the speech?

You should write about:

• sentence length

• use of repetitive structures

• the final sentences in paragraphs 4 and 5

• the penultimate sentence. (6 marks)

....

....

....

....

....

....

....

....

....

....

....

....

....

....

....

....

Score   / 10

Total score   / 22

How well did you do?   ✗ 0–6 **Try again**   7–10 **Getting there**   11–14 **Good work**   15–22 **Excellent!** ✓

For more help on this topic see **KS3 English Success Guide pages 26–29.**

Media texts

This leaflet was produced by a large supermarket chain to encourage healthy eating. It gives information about the benefits of healthy eating and recommendations about daily intake of fruit and vegetables. It also aims to persuade shoppers to buy produce from their supermarket chain.

Healthy Eating with Fruit and Vegetables

If you have been put off changing the way you eat because healthy eating advice in the past has told you what you should not eat, here's the good news. There are many delicious foods that you can eat more of - fruit and vegetables.

Fruit and vegetables are full of vitamins, minerals and fibre which are needed to maintain good health. They are also very low in fat.

Experts agree a diet low in fat and rich in fruit and vegetables (as well as starchy foods such as potatoes, bread, pasta, rice and other cereals), is best for health. So eating more fruit and vegetables helps you gain a healthier balance of foods.

Servings

Five servings can easily fit into a normal day's eating as shown below.
Don't count potatoes in your five-a-day total because although it is a good idea to eat more of them, they are classified as starchy foods along with pasta, bread, rice and other cereals.

Breakfast - glass of unsweetened fruit juice (which counts as a serving of fruit), and/or fresh fruit chopped onto your breakfast cereal = 1-2 servings

Mid-morning - fruit instead of biscuits or confectionery = 1 serving

Lunch - salad or vegetables with your meal, or fruit instead of pudding = 1-2 servings

Evening meal - as for lunch = 1-2 servings
1 serving equals:
- 2 tablespoons vegetables
- small salad
- piece fresh fruit
- 2 tablespoons stewed or canned fruit
- glass (100ml) fruit juice

Five-a-Day!

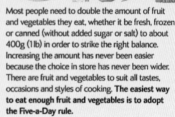

Most people need to double the amount of fruit and vegetables they eat, whether it be fresh, frozen or canned (without added sugar or salt) to about 400g (1lb) in order to strike the right balance. Increasing the amount has never been easier because the choice in store has never been wider. There are fruit and vegetables to suit all tastes, occasions and styles of cooking. **The easiest way to eat enough fruit and vegetables is to adopt the Five-a-Day rule.**

SAINSBURY'S *Where good food costs les*

Snack happy

Many people complain that it is difficult to snack healthily, but fruit in particular is the ultimate convenience or 'fast' food because much of it can be enjoyed raw and it comes wrapped in its own neat package. It doesn't take a minute to unzip a banana, which makes an excellent snack for all ages. Ring the changes by choosing fruit in season like peaches, plums and nectarines in the summer and clementines in the winter. Try dried fruit for a change - it makes an excellent snack.

- Add sliced and grated vegetables to sandwich fillings - especially good in toasted sandwiches.
- Add grated vegetables to the meat in cottage and shepherd's pie.
- Mix mashed swede and carrot with mashed potato.
- Mix mashed or puréed fruit with yogurt or fromage frais for a quick dessert.

Children's choice

Give children a taste for vegetables and fruit early on to establish good eating habits for life.

- Fruit and vegetable purées are a good basis for weaning foods.
- Add grated carrots or chopped celery and other vegetables to mince when making home-made burgers.
- Use brightly coloured vegetables like tomatoes and sweetcorn to make funny faces on pizza bases.
- Dried fruit like raisins make useful snacks.
- Use fresh or canned fruit in fruit jellies.

Take 5!

Eating with Fruit and Vegetables

Media texts: questions

A

Choose just one answer, a, b, c or d.

1 **The purpose of this text is to** (1 mark)

a) entertain ☐

b) describe ☐

c) explain and persuade ☐

d) describe and persuade ☐

2 **The text is written in Standard English because it is aimed at** (1 mark)

a) doctors and health specialists ☐

b) children ☐

c) ordinary shoppers ☐

d) people living in the South of England ☐

3 **This leaflet contains** (1 mark)

a) facts only ☐

b) a mixture of fact and opinion ☐

c) opinions only ☐

d) instructions only ☐

4 **According to the leaflet fruit and vegetables contain lots of** (1 mark)

a) fat ☐

b) starch ☐

c) protein ☐

d) vitamins ☐

5 **Which of the following shouldn't be counted in the daily allowance of fruit and vegetables?** (1 mark)

a) potatoes ☐

b) canned fruit ☐

c) frozen vegetables ☐

d) dried fruit ☐

Score / 5

B

Answer all parts of all questions.

1 **Which verb form is used in the 'Children's choice' section of the leaflet? Explain why this form is used.** (2 marks)

Verb form: ....

Explanation: ....

2 **Identify two layout/presentation features in the leaflet and explain why they have been used.** (2 marks)

Layout: ....

Explanation: ....

Layout: ....

Explanation: ....

3 **'Take 5!' is a common expression. Explain why it is an appropriate title for this text.** (3 marks)

....

....

....

....

Score / 7

C

1 **How does the leaflet aim to persuade people to buy and eat more fruit and vegetables?**

You should write about:

- the language used
- the layout of the leaflet
- whether you think the leaflet will be successful.

(10 marks)

....
....
....
....
....
....
....
....
....
....
....
....
....
....

....
....
....
....
....
....
....
....
....

Score   / 10

Total score   / 22

How well did you do? ✗ 0–6 **Try again** 7–10 **Getting there** 11–14 **Good work** 15–22 **Excellent!**

For more help on this topic see KS3 English Success Guide pages 36–43.

41

Writing to describe

A

Choose just one answer, a, b, c or d/true or false.

1 **Descriptive writing is** (1 mark)
- a) always factual ☐
- b) always fiction ☐
- c) always a balance of fact and fiction ☐
- d) can be a mixture of fact and fiction ☐

2 **An adverb** (1 mark)
- a) describes a noun ☐
- b) usually ends in *ed* ☐
- c) describes a verb ☐
- d) is a doing word ☐

3 **When you are describing a person you should concentrate on what *he/she* looks like.** (1 mark)
true/false

4 **Imagery such as simile and metaphor can be used in description.** (1 mark)
true/false

5 **Sensory description is writing that** (1 mark)
- a) describes your senses ☐
- b) describes what you can see ☐
- c) describes what you can hear ☐
- d) describes what you can see, hear, touch, taste or smell ☐

Score   / 5

B

Use the space below to complete a spider diagram plan for the writing task in Section C.

Although this section doesn't carry a score, it will help you to score higher marks in Section C.

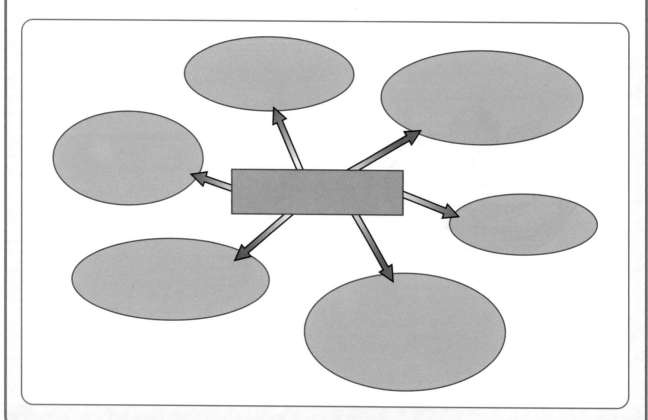

42

C

This is a SATs-style question. Your answer should respond to each of the bullet points. You should spend about 20 minutes writing. Continue your writing on a separate sheet if necessary.

1 Write a brief description of your ideal holiday location. Write three paragraphs only.

You could describe:
- the setting
- the atmosphere
- the people.

Remember to use descriptive vocabulary and imagery; try to appeal to the senses. (20 marks)

....
....
....
....
....
....
....
....
....
....
....
....
....
....
....

....
....
....
....
....
....
....
....
....

Score   / 20

Total score   / 25

How well did you do?   ✗ 0–7 Try again   8–11 Getting there   12–16 Good work   17–25 Excellent! ✓

For more help on this topic see **KS3 English Success Guide pages 54–55.**

Writing to imagine, explore, entertain

A

Choose just one answer, a, b, c or d/true or false.

1 The structure of narrative writing is
usually **(1 mark)**

a) introduction, development, resolution,
climax ☐

b) resolution, climax, introduction,
development ☐

c) introduction, development, climax,
resolution ☐

d) introduction, climax, development,
resolution ☐

2 The most important element(s) of
narrative fiction is/are **(1 mark)**

a) plot, description and dialogue ☐

b) plot ☐

c) dialogue ☐

d) plot and dialogue ☐

3 An adjective **(1 mark)**

a) usually ends in *ly* ☐

b) describes a noun ☐

c) describes a verb ☐

d) usually ends in *ed* ☐

4 You should reveal everything about a
character directly. **(1 mark)**

true/false

5 Dialogue should always be followed by a
phrase such as 'Jamie said' to indicate
who has spoken. **(1 mark)**

true/false

Score   / 5

B

Use the space below to complete a plan for the writing task in Section C.

Although this section doesn't carry a score, it will help you to score higher marks in Section C.

Main character factfile

....

....

....

....

....

....

....

....

....

Introduction

....

....

Development

....

....

Climax

....

....

Resolution

....

....

C

This is a SATs-style question. The bullet points are suggestions to help you complete the task. You should spend about 40 minutes writing. You should continue your writing on a separate sheet. Try not to write more than two sides of A4 paper.

Some of the 'Reading fiction' extracts in this book are about frightening experiences.

1 **Imagine that you are trapped somewhere. Write the story of your escape.**

You could:

• describe the place where you are trapped

• describe your feelings

• build up a tense or frightening atmosphere

• write about somebody else being trapped, if you prefer to write in the third person.

Remember to include a balance of plot development, description and dialogue. (30 marks)

....

....

....

....

....

....

....

....

....

....

....

....

....

....

....

....

....

....

....

....

....

....

Score   / 30

Total score   / 35

How well did you do?   ✗ 0–10 **Try again**   11–20 **Getting there**   21–25 **Good work**   26–35 **Excellent!** ✓

For more help on this topic see KS3 English Success Guide pages 46–51.

Writing to argue and persuade

A

Choose just one answer, a, b, c or d/true or false.

1 **Opinions would not be used in persuasive writing.** (1 mark)

true/false

2 **A counter-argument is** (1 mark)

a) a point that supports the main argument ☐

b) a point that opposes the main argument ☐

c) an argument that offends somebody ☐

d) an irrelevant point ☐

3 **Which of the following could be used as a rhetorical question?** (1 mark)

a) What is your name? ☐

b) What do you mean? ☐

c) If you feel the same way why don't you join us? ☐

d) What is your favourite colour? ☐

4 **If you begin a formal letter *Dear Sir* you should end with** (1 mark)

a) *Yours sincerely* ☐

b) *Yours faithfully* ☐

c) *Best wishes* ☐

d) *yours sincerely* ☐

5 **When hand writing a letter your own address should be written** (1 mark)

a) at the top right ☐

b) at the bottom right ☐

c) at the top left ☐

d) under the recipient's address ☐

Score   / 5

B

Use the space below to complete a plan for the writing task in Section C.

Although this section doesn't carry a score, it will help you to score higher marks in Section C.

Use this space to record and organise the main points of your argument.

Points in favour of my argument

....

....

....

....

Use this space to note down emotive words/phrases, rhetorical questions, etc.

Word/phrase bank

....

....

....

....

C

This is a SATs-style question. The bullet points are suggestions to help you complete the task. You should spend about 40 minutes writing. You should continue your writing on a separate sheet. Try not to write more than two sides of A4 paper.

1 Write a letter to your local MP to persuade him/her to support your argument that more major sporting events should take place in the UK.

You could write about:

- the benefits for British sportsmen and sportswomen
- the benefits for local communities
- the international profile of the UK
- possible objections and how you would counter them.

Remember to write a formal letter. Try to be as persuasive as you can.   (30 marks)

....
....
....
....
....
....
....
....
....
....
....
....
....
....
....
....
....
....
....
....

Score   / 30

Total score   / 35

How well did you do?   ✗ 0–10 **Try again**   11–20 **Getting there**   21–25 **Good work**   26–35 **Excellent!** ✓

For more help on this topic see **KS3 English Succe1ss Guide** pages 56–57.

Writing to inform and explain

A

Choose just one answer, a, b, c or d/true or false.

1 Information texts are usually written in the first person. (1 mark)

true/false

2 Information and explanation texts are usually written in the present tense. (1 mark)

true/false

3 Explanation texts use logical connectives. Which of the following is *not* a logical connective? (1 mark)

a) because ☐

b) as a result of ☐

c) however ☐

d) firstly ☐

4 Which of the following sentence types do information texts use? (1 mark)

a) mostly complex ☐

b) mostly simple ☐

c) simple and compound ☐

d) compound and complex ☐

5 Explanation texts sometimes use the passive voice. Which of the following doesn't use the passive voice? (1 mark)

a) The window was broken. ☐

b) John broke the window. ☐

c) The window was broken by John. ☐

d) The window was broken accidentally. ☐

Score /5

B

Use the space below to complete a plan for the writing task in Section C.

Although this section doesn't carry a score, it will help you to score higher marks in Section C.

Use this space to brainstorm information about teenage fashion.

Make brief notes to explain why different people choose different styles.

Explanation: ....

....

....

....

C

This is a SATs-style question. Your answer should respond to each of the bullet points. You should spend about 20 minutes writing. Continue your writing on a separate sheet if necessary.

Fashions change very quickly and different groups of people like to wear different styles of clothing.

1 **Write three paragraphs to inform the reader about current teenage fashion and explain why different people choose to follow different fashions.**

You could write about:

• clothes and hairstyles

• the influence of music and celebrities on fashion.

Remember to write in the third person and present tense. (20 marks)

....
....
....
....
....
....
....
....
....
....

....
....
....
....
....
....
....
....
....
....
....

Score   / 20

Total score   / 25

How well did you do?   ✗   0–7 Try again   8–11 Getting there   12–16 Good work   17–25 Excellent!   ✓

For more help on this topic see KS3 English Success Guide pages 52–53.

Writing to review, analyse, comment

A

Choose just one answer, a, b, c or d/true or false.

1 A review should contain   (1 mark)
   a) fact only ☐
   b) fact and opinion ☐
   c) opinion only ☐
   d) opinion presented as fact ☐

   c) long quotations without explanation ☐
   d) unsupported opinions ☐

2 A review should explore the strengths and weaknesses of the piece being reviewed. (1 mark)

   true/false

4 Analysis texts should be written in the   (1 mark)
   a) first person ☐
   b) second person ☐
   c) first and third person ☐
   d) third person ☐

3 Comment and analysis texts should contain   (1 mark)
   a) statements and explanations ☐
   b) statements and explanations supported by textual evidence ☐

5 Review texts can be written in the first or third person.   (1 mark)

   true/false

Score   / 5

B

Use the space below to complete a plan for the writing task in Section C.

Although this section doesn't carry a score, it will help you to score higher marks in Section C.

Make brief notes under the following headings:

Strengths

....
....
....

Weaknesses

....
....
....

Recommendations

....
....
....
....

C

This is a SATs-style question. Your answer should respond to each of the bullet points. You should spend about 20 minutes writing. Continue your writing on a separate sheet if necessary.

1 Write a brief review of a book you have read or a film you have seen recently. Write three paragraphs only.

You could include:

• information about the book/film

• the strengths of the book/film

• the weaknesses of the book/film

• your recommendations to other readers/viewers. (20 marks)

....

....

....

....

....

....

....

....

....

....

....

....

....

....

....

....

....

....

....

....

....

....

Score   / 20

Total score   / 25

How well did you do? ✗ 0–7 Try again   8–11 Getting there   12–16 Good work   17–25 Excellent! ✓

For more help on this topic see **KS3 English Success Guide** pages 58–59.

Read the two extracts from the play carefully and answer the questions that follow.

In this scene Don John convinces Claudio and Don Pedro that Hero has been unfaithful before the wedding night. He tells them he can show them the evidence of her disloyalty if they go with him.

Act III Scene 2 lines 59–end

Enter DON JOHN *the Bastard*

DON JOHN	My lord and brother, God save you.	
DON PEDRO	Good den, brother.	60
DON JOHN	If your leisure served, I would speak with you.	
DON PEDRO	In private?	
DON JOHN	If it please you, yet Count Claudio may hear, for what I would speak of, concerns him.	
DON PEDRO	What's the matter?	
DON JOHN	Means your lordship to be married tomorrow?	
DON PEDRO	You know he does.	
DON JOHN	I know not that, when he knows what I know.	
CLAUDIO	If there be any impediment, I pray you discover it.	
DON JOHN	You may think I love you not, let that appear hereafter, and aim better at me by that I now will manifest, for my brother (I think he holds you well, and in dearness of heart) hath help to effect your ensuing marriage: surely suit ill-spent, and labour ill-bestowed.	70
DON PEDRO	Why what's the matter?	
DON JOHN	I came hither to tell you, and circumstances shortened (for she has been too long a-talking of), the lady is disloyal.	
CLAUDIO	Who Hero?	
DON JOHN	Even she, Leonato's Hero, your Hero, every man's Hero.	
CLAUDIO	Disloyal?	
DON JOHN	The word is too good to paint out her wickedness, I could say she were worse, think you of a worse title, and I will fit her to it: wonder not till further warrant: go but with me tonight, you shall see her chamber window entered, even the night before her wedding day: if you love her, then tomorrow wed her: but it would better fit your honour to change your mind.	80
CLAUDIO	May this be so?	
DON PEDRO	I will not think it.	
DON JOHN	If you dare not trust that you see, confess not that you know: if you will follow me, I will show you enough: and when you have seen more, and heard more, proceed accordingly.	90
CLAUDIO	If I see anything tonight, why I should not marry her tomorrow in the congregation, where I should wed, there will I shame her.	

DON PEDRO	And as I wooed for thee to obtain her, I will join with thee, to disgrace her.
DON JOHN	I will disparage her no farther, till you are my witnesses: bear it coldly but till midnight, and let the issue show itself.
DON PEDRO	Oh day untowardly turned!
CLAUDIO	Oh mischief strangely thwarting!
DON JOHN	Oh plague right well prevented! So will you say, when you have seen the sequel.

100

Exeunt

Glossary	Good den: Good evening.
	Impediment: barrier, reason against.
	Suit ill-spent: effort wasted.
	Warrant: proof.
	Bear it coldly: control your feelings.

In this scene Claudio refuses to marry Hero, claiming that she has been unfaithful before their marriage. The men reveal what they saw the night before and Hero faints with grief.

Act IV Scene 1 lines 1–105
A church

Enter DON PEDRO, DON JOHN, LEONATO, FRIAR FRANCIS, CLAUDIO, BENEDICK, HERO *and* BEATRICE; *Wedding Guests*

LEONATO	Come, Friar Francis, be brief, only to the plain form of marriage, and you shall recount their particular duties afterwards.
FR FRANCIS	You come hither, my lord, to marry this lady?
CLAUDIO	No.
LEONATO	To be married to her: friar, you come to marry her.
FR FRANCIS	Lady, you come hither to be married to this count?
HERO	I do.
FR FRANCIS	If either of you know any inward impediment why you should not be conjoined, I charge you on your souls to utter it.
CLAUDIO	Know you any, Hero?
HERO	None, my lord.
FR FRANCIS	Know you any, count?
LEONATO	I dare make his answer, none.
CLAUDIO	Oh what men dare do! What men may do! What men daily do, not knowing what they do!
BENEDICK	How now! Interjections? Why then, some be of laughing, as, ah, ha, he.
CLAUDIO	Stand thee by, friar: father, by your leave, Will you with free and unconstrainèd soul Give me this maid your daughter?
LEONATO	As freely, son, as God did give her me.
CLAUDIO	And what have I to give you back, whose worth May counterpoise this rich and precious gift?

10

20

DON PEDRO	Nothing, unless you render her again.
CLAUDIO	Sweet prince, you learn me noble thankfulness:
	There, Leonato, take her back again,
	Give not this rotten orange to your friend,
	She's but the sign and semblance of her honour:
	Behold how like a maid she blushes here!
	Oh what authority and show of truth
	Can cunning sin cover itself withal!
	Comes not that blood, as modest evidence,
	To witness simple virtue? Would you not swear
	All you that see her, that she were a maid,
	By these exterior shows? But she is none:
	She knows the heat of a luxurious bed:
	Her blush is guiltiness, not modesty.
LEONATO	What do you mean, my lord?
CLAUDIO	Not to be married,
	Not to knit my soul to an approvèd wanton.
LEONATO	Dear my lord, if you in your own proof,
	Have vanquished the resistance of her youth,
	And made defeat of her virginity –
CLAUDIO	I know what you would say: if I have known her,
	You will say, she did embrace me as a husband,
	And so extenuate the forehand sin: no, Leonato,
	I never tempted her with word too large,
	But as a brother to his sister, showed
	Bashful sincerity, and comely love.
HERO	And seemed I ever otherwise to you?
CLAUDIO	Out on thee seeming, I will write against it!
	You seem to me as Dian in her orb,
	As chaste as is the bud ere it be blown:
	But you are more intemperate in your blood,
	Than Venus, or those pampered animals,
	That rage in savage sensuality.
HERO	Is my lord well, that he doth speak so wide?
LEONATO	Sweet prince, why speak not you?
DON PEDRO	What should I speak?
	I stand dishonoured that have gone about
	To link my dear friend to a common stale.
LEONATO	Are these things spoken, or do I but dream?
DON JOHN	Sir, they are spoken, and these things are true.
BENEDICK	This looks not like a nuptial.
HERO	True, oh God!
CLAUDIO	Leonato, stand I here?
	Is this the prince? Is this the prince's brother?
	Is this face Hero's? Are our eyes our own?
LEONATO	All this is so, but what of this, my lord?
CLAUDIO	Let me but move one question to your daughter,
	And by that fatherly and kindly power,
	That you have in her, bid her answer truly.

30

40

50

60

LEONATO	I charge thee do so, as thou art my child.	70
HERO	Oh God defend me, how am I beset!	
	What kind of catechising call you this?	
CLAUDIO	To make you answer truly to your name.	
HERO	Is it not Hero? Who can blot that name	
	With any just reproach?	
CLAUDIO	Marry that can Hero,	
	Hero itself can blot out Hero's virtue.	
	What man was he, talked with you yesternight,	
	Out at your window betwixt twelve and one?	
	Now if you are a maid, answer to this.	
HERO	I talked with no man at that hour, my lord.	80
DON PEDRO	Why then are you no maiden. Leonato,	
	I am sorry you must hear: upon mine honour,	
	Myself, my brother, and this grievèd count	
	Did see her, hear her, at that hour last night,	
	Talk with a ruffian at her chamber window,	
	Who hath indeed most like a liberal villain,	
	Confessed the vile encounters they have had	
	A thousand times in secret.	
DON JOHN	Fie, fie, they are	
	Not to be named my lord, not to be spoke of,	
	There is not chastity enough in language,	90
	Without offence to utter them: thus, pretty lady,	
	I am sorry for thy much misgovernment.	
CLAUDIO	Oh Hero! What a hero hadst thou been,	
	If half thy outward graces had been placed	
	About thy thoughts and counsels of thy heart?	
	But fare thee well, most foul, most fair, farewell	
	Thou pure impiety, and impious purity,	
	For thee I'll lock up all the gates of love,	
	And on my eyelids shall conjecture hang,	
	To turn all beauty into thoughts of harm,	100
	And never shall it more be gracious.	
LEONATO	Hath no man's dagger here a point for me?	
	[Hero faints]	
BEATRICE	Why how now, cousin, wherefore sink you down?	
DON JOHN	Come let us go: these things come thus to light,	
	Smother her spirits up.	
	[Exeunt Don Pedro, Don John and Claudio]	

Glossary Unconstrained: unforced, free.
Counterpoise: balance.
Luxurious: lustful.
Dian: goddess of the moon and chastity.
Venus: goddess of love.
Stale: prostitute.
Catechising: questioning.

Much Ado About Nothing: questions

All of the questions that follow relate to Act III Scene 2

A Choose just one answer, a, b, c or d.

1 Don John has worrying news for (1 mark)
a) Don Pedro ☐
b) Claudio ☐
c) Hero ☐
d) Benedick ☐

c) marry Hero ☐
d) confront Hero ☐

4 Claudio plans to (1 mark)
a) put the wedding off until he can speak to Hero ☐
b) marry Hero whatever he sees ☐
c) cancel the wedding ☐
d) shame Hero in public if she has been unfaithful ☐

2 Don John says that his brother's effort to arrange the marriage was (1 mark)
a) a waste of time ☐
b) a kind act ☐
c) a cruel act ☐
d) none of his business ☐

5 Don Pedro says he will (1 mark)
a) support Hero ☐
b) support Don John ☐
c) support Claudio ☐
d) speak to Leonato ☐

3 Don John wants Claudio to (1 mark)
a) watch Hero's window with him ☐
b) climb through Hero's window ☐

Score / 5

B Answer all parts of all questions.

1 When Don John says 'I know not that, when he knows what I know', what effect does this have? (2 marks)

....

....

....

2 What is the effect of repeating Hero's name in line 78 and why does Don John refer to Hero as 'every man's Hero'? (2 marks)

....

....

....

3 Explain how the pattern of sentences from 'If you dare not trust' shows how the three men begin to unite in anger. (3 marks)

....

....

....

Score / 7

C This is a SATs-style question. Your answer should respond to each of the bullet points.

1 **How does Shakespeare create a sense of growing anger in this extract?**

You should write about:

- what Don John says
- the way Claudio and Don Pedro react to what they are told
- the patterns of language used.

(10 marks)

....

....

....

....

....

....

....

....

....

....

....

....

....

....

....

....

....

....

....

....

....

....

....

....

Score **/ 10**

Total score **/ 22**

How well did you do? ✗ 0–6 **Try again** 7–10 **Getting there** 11–14 **Good work** 15–22 **Excellent!** ✓

For more help on this topic see **KS3 English Success Guide pages 66–75.**

Much Ado About Nothing: questions

All of the questions that follow relate to Act IV Scene 1

A   Choose just one answer, a, b, c or d.

1 **At the beginning of the scene Leonato tells the Friar to**   (1 mark)

a) get through the marriage service quickly ☐

b) take his time over the service ☐

c) tell them all the details of the service before proceeding ☐

d) cancel the wedding service ☐

2 **The marriage is halted because**   (1 mark)

a) Hero refuses Claudio ☐

b) Claudio refuses Hero ☐

c) Leonato refuses to give his daughter away ☐

d) Benedick objects ☐

3 **Claudio says Hero is blushing because**   (1 mark)

a) she is excited ☐

b) she is innocent ☐

c) she is guilty ☐

d) she is too hot ☐

4 **Claudio says Hero is an 'approved wanton' because**   (1 mark)

a) she slept with him before they were married ☐

b) she slept with Don John ☐

c) she slept with Don Pedro ☐

d) he and Don Pedro saw her with another man ☐

5 **At the end of the extract Leonato**   (1 mark)

a) believes Hero ☐

b) believes Claudio ☐

c) doesn't know what to believe ☐

d) blames Don John ☐

Score   / 5

B   Answer all parts of all questions.

1 **Look at Claudio's speech beginning 'Sweet prince, you learn me'.**

Find an example of a metaphor used to describe Hero and give two reasons why it is effective.   (3 marks)

Metaphor: ....

Reason: ....

Reason: ....

2 **Whose reputation is Don Pedro most concerned about? Find a quotation to support your answer.**   (2 marks)

....

....

....

3 **Find an example of word-play using contradictions (an oxymoron) in Claudio's final speech and explain its effect.**   (2 marks)

Example: ....

Explanation: ....

....

Score   / 7

C

1 **How does Shakespeare create sympathy for Hero in this extract?**

You should write about:

• what Claudio says about her

• what Hero says and how she behaves

• the way other characters behave.

(10 marks)

....

....

....

....

....

....

....

....

....

....

....

....

....

....

....

....

....

....

....

....

....

....

....

Score **/ 10**

Total score **/ 22**

How well did you do? ✗ 0–6 **Try again** 7–10 **Getting there** 11–14 **Good work** 15–22 **Excellent!** ✓

For more help on this topic see KS3 English Success Guide pages 66–75.

Richard III

Read the two extracts from the play carefully and answer the questions that follow.

In this scene Richard compares the activities of wartime and peacetime. He states his intention to be evil and begins to reveal his plans to destroy his family.

Act I Scene 1 lines 1–122
Outside the Tower of London

Enter RICHARD DUKE OF GLOUCESTER

RICHARD Now is the winter of our discontent
Made glorious summer by this son of York,
And all the clouds that loured upon our house
In the deep bosom of the ocean buried.
Now are our brows bound with victorious
   wreaths,
Our bruisèd arms hung up for monuments,
Our stern alarums changed to merry meetings,
Our dreadful marches to delightful measures.
Grim-visaged war hath smoothed his wrinkled
   front,
And now, instead of mounting barbèd steeds 10
To fright the souls of fearful adversaries,
He capers nimbly in a lady's chamber
To the lascivious pleasing of a lute.
But I that am not shaped for sportive tricks
Nor made to court an amorous looking-glass,
I that am rudely stamped and want love's
   majesty
To strut before a wanton ambling nymph,
I that am curtailed of this fair proportion,
Cheated of feature by dissembling nature,
Deformed, unfinished, sent before my time   20
Into this breathing world scarce half made up,
And that so lamely and unfashionable
That dogs bark at me as I halt by them,
Why, I in this weak piping time of peace,
Have no delight to pass away the time,
Unless to see my shadow in the sun
And descant on mine own deformity.
And, therefore, since I cannot prove a lover
To entertain these fair well-spoken days,
I am determined to prove a villain   30
And hate the idle pleasures of these days.

Plots have I laid, inductions dangerous,
By drunken prophecies, libels, and dreams
To set my brother Clarence and the king
In deadly hate the one against the other.
And if King Edward be as true and just
As I am subtle, false, and treacherous,
This day should Clarence closely be mewed up
About a prophecy which says that 'G'
Of Edward's heirs the murderer shall be.   40
Dive, thoughts, down to my soul, here Clarence
   comes.

Enter CLARENCE *guarded by* BRAKENBURY

Brother, good day. What means this armèd guard
That waits upon your grace?
CLARENCE His majesty,
Tend'ring my person's safety, hath appointed
This conduct to convey me to the Tower.
RICHARD Upon what cause?
CLARENCE Because my name is George.
RICHARD Alack, my lord, that fault is none of
   yours.
He should for that commit your godfathers.
Oh, belike his majesty hath some intent
That you should be new christened in the Tower.
   50
But what's the matter, Clarence? May I know?
CLARENCE Yea, Richard, when I know, but I
   protest
As yet I do not. But as I can learn,
He hearkens after prophecies and dreams,
And from the cross-row plucks the letter 'G',
And says a wizard told him that by 'G'
His issue disinherited should be.
And for my name of George begins with 'G',
It follows in his thought that I am he.
These, as I learn, and suchlike toys as these 60

Hath moved his highness to commit me now.

RICHARD Why, this it is when men are ruled by women.

'Tis not the king that sends you to the Tower.
My lady Grey, his wife, Clarence, 'tis she
That tempts him to this harsh extremity.
Was it not she and that good man of worship,
Anthony Woodville, her brother there,
That made him send Lord Hastings to the Tower,
From whence this present day he is delivered?
We are not safe, Clarence, we are not safe.   70

CLARENCE By heaven, I think there is no man secure
But the queen's kindred, and night-walking heralds
That trudge betwixt the king and Mistress Shore.
Heard you not what an humble suppliant
Lord Hastings was for her delivery?

RICHARD Humbly complaining to her deity
Got my lord Chamberlain his liberty.
I'll tell you what, I think it is our way,
If we will keep in favour with the king,
To be her men and wear her livery.   80
The jealous, o'er-worn widow and herself,
Since that our brother dubbed them gentlewomen,
Are mighty gossips in our monarchy.

BRAKENBURY I beseech your graces both to pardon me;
His majesty hath straitly given in charge
That no man shall have private conference,
Of what degree soever, with your brother.

RICHARD Even so. And please your worship, Brakenbury,
You may partake of any thing we say.
We speak no treason, man. We say the king   90
Is wise and virtuous, and his noble queen
Well struck in years, fair, and not jealous.
We say that Shore's wife hath a pretty foot,
A cherry lip, a bonny eye, a passing pleasing tongue,
And that the queen's kindred are made gentlefolks.
How say you, sir? Can you deny all this?

BRAKENBURY With this, my lord, myself have naught to do.

RICHARD Naught to do with Mistress Shore? I tell thee, fellow,
He that doth naught with her (excepting one)
Were best to do it secretly alone.   100

BRAKENBURY What one, my lord?

RICHARD Her husband, knave. Wouldst thou betray me?

BRAKENBURY I do beseech your grace to pardon me, and withal
Forbear your conference with the noble duke.

CLARENCE We know thy charge, Brakenbury, and will obey.

RICHARD We are the queen's abjects and must obey.
Brother, farewell, I will unto the king,
And whatsoe'er you will employ me in,
Were it to call King Edward's widow 'sister',
I will perform it to enfranchise you.   110
Meantime, this deep disgrace in brotherhood
Touches me deeper than you can imagine.

CLARENCE I know it pleaseth neither of us well.

RICHARD Well, your imprisonment shall not be long.
I will deliver you or else lie for you.
Meantime, have patience.

CLARENCE I must perforce. Farewell.

Exeunt CLARENCE, BRAKENBURY, *and guards*

RICHARD Go, tread the path that thou shalt ne'er return.
Simple, plain Clarence, I do love thee so
That I will shortly send thy soul to heaven,   120
If heaven will take the present at our hands.
But who comes here? The new-delivered Hastings?

Glossary   Loured: scowled.
Measures: dances.
Lascivious: lustful.
Descant: comment, sing about.
Inductions: preparations.
Mewed up: imprisoned.
Conduct: guard.
Cross-row: alphabet.
Livery: uniform.
Abjects: outcasts.

Act II Scene 1

In this scene King Edward had been reconciling his family and invites Richard to join in making peace. Richard does this but then announces Clarence's death and blames the Woodvilles. King Edward is angry with himself and others that nobody pleaded for Clarence's pardon.

Act II Scene 1 lines 47–end

Enter RATCLIFFE *and* RICHARD

RICHARD Good morrow to my sovereign king and
    queen;
And princely peers, a happy time of day.
KING EDWARD Happy indeed, as we have spent
    the day.
Gloucester, we have done deeds of charity,   50
Made peace of enmity, fair love of hate,
Between these swelling, wrong-incensèd peers.
RICHARD A blessèd labour, my most sovereign
    lord.
Among this princely heap, if any here
By false intelligence or wrong surmise
Hold me a foe; if I unwillingly, or in my rage
Have aught committed that is hardly borne
To any in this presence, I desire
To reconcile me to his friendly peace.
'Tis death to me to be at enmity;   60
I hate it and desire all good men's love.
First, madam, I entreat true peace of you,
Which I will purchase with my duteous service;
Of you, my noble cousin Buckingham,
If ever any grudge were lodged between us;
Of you and you, Lord Rivers, and of Dorset,
That all without desert have frowned on me;
Of you, Lord Woodville, and Lord Scales, of you;
Dukes, earls, lords, gentlemen, indeed of all.
I do not know that Englishman alive   70
With whom my soul is any jot at odds
More than the infant that is born tonight.
I thank my God for my humility.
ELIZABETH A holy day shall this be kept
    hereafter.
I would to God all strifes were well compounded.
My sovereign lord, I do beseech your highness
To take our brother Clarence to your grace.
RICHARD Why, madam, have I offered love for
    this,

To be so flouted in this royal presence?
Who knows not that the gentle duke is dead?   80
    [*They all start*]
You do him injury to scorn his corpse.
KING EDWARD Who knows not he is dead?
Who knows he is?
ELIZABETH All-seeing heaven, what a world is
    this?
BUCKINGHAM Look I so pale, Lord Dorset, as the
    rest?
DORSET Ay, my good lord, and no man in the
    presence
But his red colour hath forsook his cheeks.
KING EDWARD Is Clarence dead? The order was
    reversed.
RICHARD But he (poor man) by your first order
    died,
And that a wingèd Mercury did bear;   90
Some tardy cripple bare the countermand,
That came too lag to see him burièd.
God grant that some, less noble and less loyal,
Nearer in bloody thoughts and not in blood,
Deserve not worse than wretched Clarence did,
And yet go current from suspicion.

Enter [STANLEY] EARL OF DERBY

STANLEY A boon, my sovereign, for my service
    done.
KING EDWARD I prithee, peace, my soul is full of
    sorrow.
STANLEY I will not rise unless your highness hear
    me.
KING EDWARD Then say at once what is it thou
    requests.   100
STANLEY The forfeit, sovereign, of my servant's
    life,
Who slew today a riotous gentleman
Lately attendant on the Duke of Norfolk.

KING EDWARD Have I a tongue to doom my
  brother's death,
And shall that tongue give pardon to a slave?
My brother killed no man; his fault was thought,
And yet his punishment was bitter death.
Who sued to me for him? Who (in my wrath)
Kneeled at my feet and bid me be advised?
Who spoke of brotherhood? Who spoke
  of love? 110
Who told me how the poor soul did forsake
The mighty Warwick and did fight for me?
Who told me, in the field at Tewkesbury,
When Oxford had me down, he rescued me
And said 'Dear brother, live, and be a king'?
Who told me, when we both lay in the field,
Frozen almost to death, how he did lap me
Even in his garments and did give himself
(All thin and naked) to the numb cold night?
All this from my remembrance brutish wrath 120
Sinfully plucked, and not a man of you
Had so much grace to put it in my mind.
But when your carters or your waiting vassals
Have done a drunken slaughter and defaced
The precious image of our dear redeemer,
You straight are on your knees for pardon,
  pardon,

And I, unjustly too, must grant it you.
But for my brother not a man would speak,
Nor I, ungracious, speak unto myself
For him, poor soul. The proudest of you all   130
Have been beholding to him in his life,
Yet none of you would once beg for his life.
Oh God, I fear thy justice will take hold
On me and you, and mine and yours, for this.
Come, Hastings, help me to my closet.
Ah, poor Clarence!

[*Exeunt some with King and Queen*]

RICHARD This is the fruits of rashness. Marked
  you not
How that the guilty kindred of the queen
Looked pale when they did hear of Clarence'
  death?
Oh, they did urge it still unto the king.   140
God will revenge it. Come, lords, will you go
To comfort Edward with our company?
BUCKINGHAM We wait upon your grace.
    Exeunt

Glossary   Heap: company.
          False intelligence: wrong information.
          Surmise: conclusion.
          Without desert: without cause.
          Flouted: insulted, wrongly used.
          Lag: late.
          Go current: escape.
          Sued to me: pleaded with me.
          Lap: wrap.

Richard III: questions

All of the questions that follow relate to Act I Scene 1

A

Choose just one answer, a, b, c or d.

1 **Richard plans to be a villain because** (1 mark)

a) he lost the war ☐

b) he cannot be a lover ☐

c) his family has betrayed him ☐

d) he wants to start another war ☐

2 **King Edward has imprisoned Clarence because** (1 mark)

a) his name is George ☐

b) Richard told him to ☐

c) he believes Clarence will disinherit his children ☐

d) he betrayed him in the war ☐

3 **Richard tells Clarence he should blame** (1 mark)

a) the King ☐

b) himself ☐

c) Lady Grey ☐

d) Lord Hastings ☐

4 **Richard promises Clarence he will** (1 mark)

a) kill him ☐

b) free him ☐

c) take his place ☐

d) spread lies about him ☐

5 **Richard really plans to** (1 mark)

a) have Clarence killed ☐

b) save Clarence ☐

c) kill the King ☐

d) stay out of the problem ☐

Score / 5

B

Answer all parts of all questions.

1 Look at the section beginning 'Now are our brows bound' and ending 'pleasing of a lute'. Give two examples of how Shakespeare uses language to emphasise the contrast between wartime and peace. Use words and phrases from the text to support your answer. (4 marks)

....

....

....

2 Look at the section beginning 'But I that am not shaped' and ending 'as I halt by them'. Choose two words or phrases that Richard uses to describe himself and explain the effect it has.

Example:..

Explanation:...(1 mark)

Example:..

Explanation:...(1 mark)

3 Explain why Richard instructs his thoughts to 'dive' into his soul. (1 mark)

....

Score / 7

C

This is a SATs-style question. Your answer should respond to each of the bullet points.

1 **In his first soliloquy Richard declares his intention to be a villain.**
How does Shakespeare give the impression that Richard is bad in this extract?

You should write about:

• what Richard says when he is alone on stage

• the way he speaks to other characters

• the imagery Shakespeare uses.   (10 marks)

....

....

....

....

....

....

....

....

....

....

....

....

....

....

....

....

....

....

....

....

....

....

....

....

....

Score   / 10

Total score   / 22

RICHARD III

Shakespeare

How well did you do? ✗ 0–6 **Try again** 7–10 **Getting there** 11–14 **Good work** 15–22 **Excellent!** ✓

For more help on this topic see KS3 English Success Guide pages 66–75.

Richard III: questions

All of the questions that follow relate to Act II Scene 1

A

Choose just one answer, a, b, c or d.

1 **When King Edward asks Richard to make peace with the others** (1 mark)

a) he refuses ☐

b) he says that the problems have all been his fault ☐

c) he says there are no problems to be reconciled over ☐

d) he agrees, claiming that he hates arguments ☐

2 **What piece of news does Richard deliver that surprises everyone?** (1 mark)

a) Clarence is dead ☐

b) Clarence has escaped ☐

c) he has killed Clarence ☐

d) Clarence has killed himself ☐

3 **Stanley pleads with the King to** (1 mark)

a) save his life ☐

b) pardon Clarence ☐

c) save his servant's life ☐

d) execute his servant ☐

4 **King Edward is angry with** (1 mark)

a) himself because he ordered Clarence's death ☐

b) the Woodvilles (the Queen's family) ☐

c) his family because they didn't plead for Clarence's life ☐

d) a and c ☐

5 **Who does Richard blame for Clarence's death?** (1 mark)

a) King Edward ☐

b) himself ☐

c) the Woodvilles ☐

d) Hastings and Buckingham ☐

Score / 5

B

Answer all parts of all questions.

1 Look at the section beginning 'Among this princely heap' and ending 'all good men's love'. Explain how Richard tries to show that he wants peace. (2 marks)

....

....

2 What does Richard do to disrupt the feeling of peace and goodwill in this scene? (1 mark)

....

....

3 Re-read King Edward's speech beginning 'Have I a tongue'. Find two examples that show Edward feels guilty about his brother's death and explain how they show his guilt. (4 marks)

Example: ....

Explanation: ....

Example: ....

Explanation: ....

Score / 7

C This is a SATs-style question. Your answer should respond to each of the bullet points.

1 **In this extract how does Shakespeare demonstrate Richard's ability to manipulate others?**

You should write about:

• what Richard says and what he really thinks

• the timing of what Richard says

• how Edward feels about his brother's death

• how Richard uses other characters. (10 marks)

....

....

....

....

....

....

....

....

....

....

....

....

....

....

....

....

....

....

....

....

....

....

Score   / 10

Total score   / 22

How well did you do?   ✗   0–6 **Try again**   7–10 **Getting there**   11–14 **Good work**   15–22 **Excellent!** ✓

For more help on this topic see **KS3 English Success Guide pages 66–75.**

The Tempest

Read the two extracts from the play carefully and answer the questions that follow.

In this scene Caliban is complaining about Prospero. When he hears Trinculo, he hides fearing that he is one of Prospero's spirits. Trinculo is frightened of the weather and hides under Caliban's cloak. Stephano discovers Trinculo and they force Caliban to drink.

Act II Scene 2 lines 1–101

Enter CALIBAN, *with a burden of wood. A noise of thunder heard*

CALIBAN All the infections that the sun sucks up
From bogs, fens, flats, on Prosper fall, and make him
By inch-meal a disease. His spirits hear me,
And yet I needs must curse. But they'll nor pinch,
Fright me with urchin-shows, pitch me i'th'mire,
Nor lead me like a firebrand in the dark
Out of my way, unless he bid 'em; but
For every trifle are they set upon me,
Sometime like apes, that mow and chatter at me
And after bite me; then like hedgehogs, which
Lie tumbling in my barefoot way and mount
Their pricks at my footfall; sometime am I
All wound with adders, who with cloven tongues
Do hiss me into madness.

Enter TRINCULO

Lo, now lo!
Here comes a spirit of his, and to torment me
For bringing wood in slowly. I'll fall flat,
Perchance he will not mind me.
 [*He lies down, and covers himself with a cloak*]
TRINCULO Here's neither bush, nor shrub to bear off any weather at all, and another storm brewing – I hear it sing i'th'wind. Yond same black cloud, yond huge one, looks like a foul bombard that would shed his liquor. If it should thunder as it did before, I know not where to hide my head. Yond same cloud cannot choose but fall by pailfulls. [*Sees* CALIBAN] What have we here – a man, or a fish? Dead or alive? A fish, he smells like a fish; a very ancient and fishlike smell; a kind of, not-of-the-newest poor-John. A strange

fish. Were I in England now – as once I was – and had but this fish painted, not a holiday-fool there but would give a piece of silver. There, would this monster make a man; any strange beast there makes a man. When they will not give a doit to relieve a lame beggar, they will lay out ten to see a dead Indian. Legged like a man – and his fins like arms. Warm o'my troth! I do now let loose my opinion, hold it no longer: this is no fish, but an islander, that hath lately suffered by a thunderbolt. [*Thunder*] Alas, the storm is come again. My best way is to creep under his gaberdine; there is no other shelter hereabout. Misery acquaints a man with strange bedfellows. I will here shroud till the dregs of the storm be past.
 [*He hides under* CALIBAN'S *cloak*]

Enter STEPHANO [*carrying a bottle and*] *singing.*

STEPHANO I shall no more to sea, to sea, Here shall I die ashore.
This is a very scurvy tune to sing at a man's funeral. Well, here's my comfort. (*Drinks*)
(*Sings*) The master, the swabber, the boatswain and I,
The gunner, and his mate,
Loved Mall, Meg, and Marian, and Margery,
But none of us cared for Kate.
For she had a tongue with a tang,
Would cry to a sailor, 'Go hang!'
She loved not the savour of tar nor of pitch,
Yet a tailor might scratch her where'er she did itch.
Then to sea boys, and let her go hang!
This is a scurvy tune too; but here's my comfort.
 (*Drinks*)

CALIBAN Do not torment me! O!

STEPHANO What's the matter? Have we devils here? Do you put tricks upon's with savages and men of Ind? Ha? I have not 'scaped drowning to be afeared now of your four legs. For it hath been said, 'As proper a man as ever went on four legs, cannot make him give ground'; and it shall be said so again, while Stephano breathes at' nostrils.

CALIBAN The spirit torments me! O!

STEPHANO This is some monster of the isle, with four legs, who hath got, as I take it, an ague. Where the devil should he learn our language? I will give him some relief if it be but for that. If I can recover him, and keep him tame, and get to Naples with him, he's a present for any emperor that ever trod on neat's leather.

CALIBAN Do not torment me, prithee! I'll bring my wood home faster.

STEPHANO He's in his fit now, and does not talk after the wisest. He shall taste of my bottle. If he have never drunk wine afore, it will go near to remove his fit. If I can recover him, and keep him tame, I will not take too much for him; he shall pay for him that hath him, and that soundly.

CALIBAN Thou dost me yet but little hurt; thou wilt anon, I know it by thy trembling. Now Prosper works upon thee.

STEPHANO Come on your ways. Open your mouth; here is that which will give language to you, cat. Open your mouth; this will shake your shaking, I can tell you, and that soundly.

[CALIBAN *drinks and spits it out*]

You cannot tell who's your friend: open your chops again.

[CALIBAN *drinks again*]

TRINCULO I should know that voice. It should be – but he is drowned, and these are devils. O defend me!

STEPHANO Four legs and two voices; a most delicate monster! His forward voice now is to speak well of his friend; his backward voice is to utter foul speeches, and to detract. If all the wine in my bottle will recover him, I will help his ague. Come.

[CALIBAN *drinks*]

Amen. I will pour some in thy other mouth.

TRINCULO Stephano.

STEPHANO Doth thy other mouth call me? Mercy, mercy! This is a devil, and no monster. I will leave him; I have no long spoon.

TRINCULO Stephano! If thou beest Stephano, touch me, and speak to me; for I am Trinculo – be not afeared – thy good friend Trinculo.

STEPHANO If thou beest Trinculo, come forth! I'll pull thee by the lesser legs. If any be Trinculo's legs, these are they.

[*Pulls him out*]

Thou art very Trinculo indeed! How cam'st thou to be the siege of this moon-calf? Can he vent Trinculos?

TRINCULO I took him to be killed with a thunderstroke. But art thou not drowned, Stephano? I hope now thou art not drowned. Is the storm over-blown? I hid me under the dead mooncalf's gaberdine for fear of the storm. And art thou living, Stephano? O Stephano, two Neapolitans 'scaped!

[*Embraces* STEPHANO]

Glossary	
Flats:	swamp.
Inch-meal:	inch by inch.
Mow:	make faces.
Perchance:	perhaps.
Mind:	notice.
Poor-John:	salted, dried fish.
Doit:	coin.
Ague:	fever.
Siege:	excrement.
Moon-calf:	monster.

Read the two extracts from the play and answer the questions that follow.

In this scene Stephano, Trinculo and Caliban are drunk. Stephano imagines being ruler of the island and promises to make Caliban his deputy. Trinculo mocks them and Stephano threatens to hang him for mutiny. Caliban begs Stephano to kill Prospero. Ariel makes trouble for Trinculo.

Act III Scene 2 lines 1–79
Near Caliban's cave

Enter CALIBAN, STEPHANO *and* TRINCULO

STEPHANO Tell not me. When the butt is out we will drink water, not a drop before; therefore bear up, and board 'em. Servant monster, drink to me.

TRINCULO [*Aside*] Servant monster? The folly of this island! They say there's but five upon   5
this isle; we are three of them – if th'other two be brained like us, the state totters.

STEPHANO Drink, servant monster, when I bid thee; thy eyes are almost set in thy head.

TRINCULO Where should they be set else? He were a brave monster indeed if they were set in his tail.   10

STEPHANO My man-monster hath drowned his tongue in sack. For my part, the sea cannot drown me – I swam, ere I could recover the shore, five and thirty leagues off and on. By this light, thou shalt be my lieutenant, monster, or my standard.

TRINCULO Your lieutenant if you list; he's no standard.   15

STEPHANO We'll not run, monsieur monster.

TRINCULO Nor go neither; but you'll lie like dogs, and yet say nothing neither.

STEPHANO Moon-calf, speak once in thy life, if thou beest a good moon-calf.   20

CALIBAN How does thy honour? Let me lick thy shoe. I'll not serve him, he is not valiant.

TRINCULO Thou liest, most ignorant monster; I am in case to jostle a constable. Why, thou deboshed fish thou, was there ever man a coward that hath drunk so much sack as I   25
today? Wilt thou tell a monstrous lie, being but half a fish, and half a monster?

CALIBAN Lo, how he mocks me. Wilt thou let him, my lord?

TRINCULO 'Lord', quoth he? That a monster should be such a natural!   30

CALIBAN Lo, lo again! Bite him to death, I prithee.

STEPHANO Trinculo, keep a good tongue in your head. If you prove a mutineer, the next tree. The poor monster's my subject, and he shall not suffer indignity.

CALIBAN I thank my noble lord. Wilt thou be   35
pleased to hearken once again to the suit I made to thee?

STEPHANO Marry will I. Kneel, and repeat it. I will stand, and so shall Trinculo.

Enter ARIEL *invisible*

CALIBAN As I told thee before, I am subject to a tyrant, a sorcerer, that by his cunning hath   40
cheated me of the island.

ARIEL Thou liest.

CALIBAN [*To* TRINCULO] Thou liest, thou jesting monkey thou. I would my valiant master would destroy thee. I do not lie.

STEPHANO Trinculo, if you trouble him any more in's tale, by this hand, I will supplant some of your teeth.   45

TRINCULO Why, I said nothing.

STEPHANO Mum then, and no more. [*To* CALIBAN] Proceed.

CALIBAN I say by sorcery he got this isle;
From me he got it. If thy greatness will
Revenge it on him – for I know thou dar'st,   50
But this thing dare not –

STEPHANO That's most certain.

CALIBAN Thou shalt be lord of it, and I'll serve thee.

STEPHANO How now shall this be compassed? Canst thou bring me to the party?   55

CALIBAN Yea, yea, my lord, I'll yield him thee
 asleep,
 Where thou mayst knock a nail into his head.
ARIEL Thou liest, thou canst not.
CALIBAN What a pied ninny's this? [*To*
 TRINCULO] Thou scurvy patch!
 [*To* STEPHANO] I do beseech thy greatness
 give him blows, 60
 And take his bottle from him. When that's
 gone,
 He shall drink nought but brine, for I'll not
 show him
 Where the quick freshes are.
STEPHANO Trinculo, run into no further danger.
 Interrupt the monster one word further, 65
 and by this hand, I'll turn my mercy out
 o'doors, and make a stockfish of thee.

TRINCULO Why, what did I? I did nothing. I'll go
 farther off.
STEPHANO Didst thou not say he lied?
ARIEL Thou liest.
STEPHANO Do I so? 70

[*Strikes* TRINCULO]

Take thou that! As you like this, give me the lie
another time.
TRINCULO I did not give the lie. Out o'your wits,
 and hearing too? A pox o'your bottle! This can
 sack and drinking do. A murrain on your
 monster, and the devil take your fingers!
CALIBAN Ha, ha, ha! 75
STEPHANO Now forward with your tale. [*To*
 TRINCULO] Prithee stand further off.
CALIBAN Beat him enough; after a little time I'll
 beat him too.

Glossary Bear up, and board 'em: drink up (a sailors' toast).
 Brained like: as clever as.
 Set: fixed or staring.
 Standard: standard bearer (pun: able to stand).
 List: please (pun: lean over like a sinking ship).
 Deboshed: drunken.
 Natural: idiot.
 Suit: request.
 Marry: by Saint Mary.
 Supplant: uproot.
 Compassed: brought about.
 Stockfish: dried cod made soft by beating.
 Pox: curse.
 Murrain: plague.

The Tempest: questions

All of the questions that follow relate to Act II Scene 2

A

Choose just one answer, a, b, c or d.

1 Which is the correct description of the verse used in this scene? (1 mark)

a) begins in blank verse and continues in prose ☐

b) begins in prose and continues in blank verse ☐

c) the whole scene is in rhyming couplets ☐

d) the whole scene is in blank verse ☐

2 Which of the following torments is *not* suffered by Caliban? (1 mark)

a) led out of his way in the dark ☐

b) hissed at by adders ☐

c) burnt with fire ☐

d) soles of his feet pricked ☐

3 Where does Trinculo find shelter from the weather? (1 mark)

a) under his cloak ☐

b) under Caliban's cloak ☐

c) in Prospero's cell ☐

d) under a bush ☐

4 What does Stephano give to Caliban? (1 mark)

a) water ☐

b) food ☐

c) a cloak ☐

d) wine ☐

5 Which of the following statements is true? (1 mark)

a) Caliban thinks Stephano is one of Prospero's spirits ☐

b) Trinculo thinks Stephano has drowned ☐

c) Stephano thinks Caliban is dead ☐

d) a and b ☐

Score / 5

B

Answer all parts of all questions.

1 Re-read Caliban's first speech, beginning 'All the infections'.

How does he give the impression of being harshly treated by Prospero?

Support your answer with words and phrases from the text. (2 marks)

....

....

2 What does Stephano hope to do with Caliban? (1 mark)

....

3 From what they say about Caliban, how do Stephano and Trinculo show that they think he is a monster?

Support your answer with words and phrases from the text. (4 marks)

....

....

....

....

Score / 7

This is a SATs-style question. Your answer should respond to each of the bullet points.

1 **In this extract how does Shakespeare create confusion and comedy?**

You should write about:

• what Caliban says and does

• what Stephano and Trinculo say and do

• how each character is confused about the identities of the others.   (10 marks)

....

....

....

....

....

....

....

....

....

....

....

....

....

....

....

....

....

....

....

....

....

Score   / 10

Total score   / 22

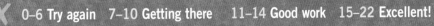

How well did you do?   0–6 **Try again**   7–10 **Getting there**   11–14 **Good work**   15–22 **Excellent!**

For more help on this topic see KS3 English Success Guide pages 66–75.

The Tempest: questions

All of the questions that follow relate to Act III Scene 2

A   Choose just one answer, a, b, c or d.

1 When Stephano threatens Trinculo with 'the next tree', what does he mean?   (1 mark)

a) he will leave him under it ☐

b) he will hang him from it ☐

c) he will hit him with a branch from it ☐

d) he will have to climb it ☐

2 'If you list' means if you please and if you are falling down. What is the name of this device?   (1 mark)

a) simile ☐

b) metaphor ☐

c) pun ☐

d) alliteration ☐

3 When Ariel is talking who do the others think it is?   (1 mark)

a) they know it's Ariel ☐

b) Caliban ☐

c) a ghost ☐

d) Trinculo ☐

4 How does Caliban claim that Prospero gained the island?   (1 mark)

a) by fighting ☐

b) by magic ☐

c) through marriage ☐

d) by killing the previous ruler ☐

5 What does Caliban say Trinculo will have to drink?   (1 mark)

a) salt water ☐

b) fresh water ☐

c) wine ☐

d) nothing ☐

Score   / 5

B   Answer all parts of all questions.

1 Re-read Trinculo's first speech, beginning 'Servant Monster?' What does he say about the state of the island and what does this show about his opinion of his companions?   (2 marks)

....

....

2 Find two examples to show that Stephano considers himself to be Caliban's master and two examples that show Caliban is happy to serve him.   (2 marks)

Examples: ....

Examples: ....

3 What three things does Stephano threaten Trinculo with?   (3 marks)

a)...

b)...

c)...

Score   / 7

C

1 **In this extract how does Shakespeare present the conflict between Stephano, Trinculo and Caliban?**

You should write about:

• what Trinculo says and does

• how Stephano treats Caliban and Trinculo

• what Ariel adds to the conflict. (10 marks)

....

....

....

....

....

....

....

....

....

....

....

....

....

....

....

....

....

....

....

....

....

....

Score   / 10

Total score   / 22

Spelling

A

Choose just one answer, a, b, c or d.

1 A word which sounds the same as another word but is spelt differently and has a different meaning is a **(1 mark)**
a) homograph ☐
b) homonym ☐
c) homophone ☐
d) synonym ☐

2 Words ending in *ch* are pluralised by adding **(1 mark)**
a) s ☐ b) 's ☐ c) ies ☐ d) es ☐

3 The correct spelling meaning *belonging to it* is **(1 mark)**
a) it's ☐ b) its ☐ c) its' ☐ d) it is ☐

4 *ies* is the correct plural ending of **(1 mark)**
a) all words ending in *y* ☐
b) words ending in a *vowel* then *y* ☐
c) words ending in a *consonant* then *y* ☐
d) words ending in *f* ☐

5 A group of letters added to the beginning of a word to change the meaning is **(1 mark)**
a) a suffix ☐
b) a prefix ☐
c) a synonym ☐
d) an antonym ☐

Score **/ 5**

B

Answer all parts of all questions.

1 The following words are all spelt incorrectly. Write the correct spelling next to each one. **(10 marks)**

acommodation ....

comited...

strawberrys ....

seperate ....

definate..

churche's (plural)..

leafs ....

possable ....

sucessfull...

beautyful ....

2 Pluralise the following words. **(2 marks)**

monkey   boy   factory   baby   try

....

....

....

3 Write the rule for pluralising words ending in *y*. **(1 mark)**

....

Score **/ 13**

Answer all parts of all questions.

1 There are seven spelling mistakes in the passage below. Find each mistake and write the correct spellings beneath.

(7 marks)

He undressed quickley, bending his pumps free of his heels and sliding them off without untying the laces. When he stood up the black soles of his sockes stamped damp imprints on the dry floor, witch developed into a haphazard set of footprints when he removed his socks and steped around pulling his jeans down. His ankels and knees were ingrained with ancient dirt which seemed to belong to the pigmentasion of his skin. His left leg sported a mud stripe, and both his knees were encrusted. The surfaces of these mobile crusts where hair-lined, and with every flexion of the knee these lines opened into frown-like furrows.

from *A Kestrel for a Knave*
by Barry Hines

a) ....

b) ....

c) ....

d) ....

e) ....

f) ....

g) ....

2 Choose the correct homophone for each sentence that follows.

(7 marks)

The books are on the table over their/they're/there.

Read threw/through your answers before you finish the exam.

Were/We're going on holiday next week.

I cut myself with the sore/saw and now my arm is really sore/saw.

I don't no/know what the answer is.

Did you hear/here that noise?

The not/knot is too tight.

Score   / 14

Total score   / 32

How well did you do?   ✗ 0–10 **Try again**   11–18 **Getting there**   19–24 **Good work**   25–32 **Excellent!** ✓

For more help on this topic see KS3 English Success Guide pages 78–87.

Punctuation and grammar

A

Choose just one answer, a, b, c or d.

1 **A simple sentence does *not* contain a** (1 mark)
- a) main clause ☐
- b) comma ☐
- c) verb ☐
- d) subordinate clause ☐

2 **A sentence joining two main clauses with *and* is a** (1 mark)
- a) simple sentence ☐
- b) compound sentence ☐
- c) complex sentence ☐
- d) concrete sentence ☐

3 **Which of the following cannot be used to end a sentence?** (1 mark)
- a) full stop ☐
- b) question mark ☐
- c) comma ☐
- d) exclamation mark ☐

4 **Which of the following statements is incorrect?** (1 mark)
- a) a sentence usually contains a verb ☐
- b) a sentence must begin with a capital letter ☐
- c) never begin a sentence with the word *because* ☐
- d) sentences don't always end with a full stop ☐

5 **An embedded clause** (1 mark)
- a) splits a main clause ☐
- b) ends a sentence ☐
- c) is always a main clause ☐
- d) must contain a non-finite verb ☐

Score / 5

B

Answer all parts of all questions.

1 **Change these two sentences into one compound sentence.** (1 mark)

I went to the shop. I bought a chocolate bar.

....

2 **Move the subordinate clause in the following sentence, changing the punctuation if necessary.** (2 marks)

The trains were late due to track repairs.

....

3 **Embed the subordinate clause in the following sentence, changing the punctuation if necessary.** (2 marks)

Filled with despair, the teacher marked the exam papers.

....

4 **Add apostrophes to the following.** (8 marks)

dont	whos (who is)	the poets (singular) writing	doesnt
Joannes bag	the girls (plural) bags	the girls (singular) bag	couldnt

Score / 13

78

C

Answer all parts of all questions.

1 **a) Give three reasons for beginning a new paragraph.** (3 marks)

i) ....

ii) ....

iii) ....

**b) This extract was originally written in three paragraphs. Identify where each new paragraph
should begin and end.** (3 marks)

I took a train to Liverpool. They were having a festival of litter when I arrived. Citizens had taken time
off from their busy activities to add crisp packets, empty cigarette boxes, and carrier-bags to the
otherwise bland and neglected landscape. They fluttered gaily in the bushes and brought colour and
texture to pavements and gutters. And to think that elsewhere we stick these objects in rubbish bags.
In another bout of extravagant madness, I had booked a room in the Adelphi Hotel. I had seen it from
the street on earlier visits and it appeared to have an old-fashioned grandeur about it that I was keen
to investigate. On the other hand, it looked expensive and I wasn't sure my trousers could stand
another session in the trouser press. So I was most agreeably surprised when I checked in to discover
that I was entitled to a special weekend rate and that there would be money spare for a nice meal and
a parade of beer in any of the many wonderful pubs in which Liverpool specializes. And so, soon
afterwards, I found myself, like all fresh arrivals in Liverpool, in the grand and splendorous
surroundings of the Philharmonic, clutching a pint glass . . .

from *Notes from a Small Island*
by Bill Bryson

i) ....

ii) ....

iii) ....

2 **Add the correct punctuation to the following sentences, inserting capital letters.** (8 marks)

a) when the rope snapped the climber who was very frightened fell and broke his leg

....

b) can I go out tonight mum asked Alison

....

c) when the alarm rang the workers left the building calmly

....

d) gosh exclaimed the woman I didn't see you there

....

Score   / 14

Total sc

For more help on this topic see KS3 English Success Guide pages78–79 and 88–93

Paper 1: Reading

- The paper is one hour long plus 15 minutes' reading time.
- Read the three texts provided and answer all the questions that follow.
- Answer each question in the space provided.
- The number of marks available for each task is printed next to the question.

Text 1 – Fiction

Read the three texts that follow and answer all of the questions in the reading section.

In this extract Billy Casper continues his routine to tame and train the kestrel he found when he went nesting.

Billy approached the hawk slowly, regarding it obliquely, ducking and chanting softly, 'Kes Kes Kes'. The hawk bobbed her head and shifted along the perch. Billy held out his gauntlet and offered her a scrap of beef. She reached forward and grasped it with her beak, and tried to pull it from his glove. Billy gripped the beef tightly between forefinger and thumb; and in order to obtain more leverage, the hawk stepped on to his fist. He allowed her to take the beef, then replaced her on the perch, touching the backs of her legs against the wood so that she stepped backwards on to it. He dipped into the leather satchel at his hip and offered her a fresh scrap; this time holding it just out of range of her reaching beak. She bobbed her head and tippled forward slightly, regained balance, then glanced about, uncertain, like someone up on the top board for the first time.

'Come on, Kes. Come on then.'

He stood still. The hawk looked at the meat, then jumped on to the glove and took it. Billy smiled and replaced it with a tough strip of beef, and as the hawk busied herself with it, he attached a swivel to the ends of the jesses dangling from her legs, slipped the jesses between the first and second fingers of his glove, and felt into his bag for the leash. The hawk looked up from her feeding. Billy rubbed his finger and thumb to make the meat move between them, and as the hawk attended to it again, he threaded the leash through the lower ring of the swivel and pulled it all the way through until the knot at the other end snagged on the ring. He completed the security by looping the leash twice round his glove and tying the end round his little finger.

He walked to the door and slowly pushed it open. The hawk looked up, and as he moved out into the full light, her eyes seemed to expand, her body contract as she flattened her feathers. She bobbed her head, once, twice, then bated, throwing herself sideways off his glove and hanging upside down, thrashing her wings and screaming. Billy waited for her to stop, then placed his hand gently under her breast and lifted her back on to the glove. She bated again; and again, and each time Billy lifted her carefully back up, until finally she stayed up, beak half open, panting, glaring round.

'What's up then? What's a matter with you, Kes? Anybody'd think you'd never been out
~re.'

The hawk roused her feathers and bent to her meat, her misdemeanours apparently forgotten.

Billy walked her round the garden, speaking quietly to her all the time. Then he turned up the path at the side of the house and approached the front gate, watching the hawk for her actions. A car approached. The hawk tensed, watched it then resumed her meal as it sped away up the avenue. On the opposite pavement a little boy, pedalling a tricycle round in tight circles, looked up and saw them, immediately unwound and drove straight off the pavement, making the tin mudguards clank as the wheels jonked down into the gutter. Billy held the hawk away from him, anticipating a bate, but she glanced up at the sound, or at the boy as he cycled towards them and hutched his tricycle up on the pavement.

'Oo that's a smasher. What is it?'

'What tha think it is?'

'Is it an owl?'

'It's a kestrel.'

'Where you got it from?'

'Found it.'

'Is it tame?'

'It's trained. I've trained it.'

Billy pointed to himself, and smiled across at the hawk.

'Don't it look fierce?'

'It is.'

'Does it kill things and eat 'em?'

'Course it does. It kills little kids on bikes.'

The boy laughed without smiling.

'It don't.'

'What's tha think that it's eating now then?'

'It's only a piece of meat.'

'It's a piece o' leg off a kid it caught yesterday. When it catches 'em it sits on their handlebars and rips 'em to pieces. Eyes first.'

The boy looked down at the chrome handlebars and began to swing them from side to side, making the front wheel describe a steady arc like a windscreen wiper.

'I bet I dare stroke it.'

'Tha'd better not.'

'I'll bet I dare.'

'It'll have thi hand off if tha tries.'

The boy stood up, straddling the tricycle frame, and slowly lifted one hand towards the hawk. She mantled her wings over the meat, then struck out with her scaly yellow legs, screaming and raking at the hand with her talons. The boy jerked his arm back with such force that its momentum carried his whole body over the tricycle and on to the ground. He scrambled up, as wide-eyed as the hawk, mounted and pedalled off down the pavement, his legs whirring like bee's wings.

from *A Kestrel for a Knave*
by Barry Hines

Text 2 – Non-fiction

In this extract Douglas Adams describes his experience of scuba diving in Australia, looking for giant manta rays.

For the afternoon dive, Ian said he wanted to take me in a different direction from the boat. I asked him why, and he looked non-committal. I followed him down into the water and slowly we flippered our way across to a new part of the reef. When we reached it, the flat top of the reef was about four feet below the surface, and the sunlight dappled gently over the extraordinary shapes and colours of the brain coral, the antler coral, the sea ferns and anemones. The stuff you see beneath the water often seems like a wild parody of the stuff you see above it. I remember the thought I had when first I dived on the Barrier Reef years ago, which was that this was all the stuff that people used to have on their mantelpieces in the fifties. It took me a while to rid myself of the notion that the reef was a load of kitsch.

I've never learnt the names of a lot of fish. I always swot them up on the boat and forget them a week later. But watching the breathtaking variety of shape and movement keeps me entranced for hours, or would if the oxygen allowed. If I were not an atheist, I think I would have to be a Catholic because if it wasn't the forces of natural selection that designed fish, it must have been an Italian.

I was moving forward slowly in the shallows. A few feet in front of me the reef gradually dipped down into a broad valley. The valley floor was wide and dark and flat. Ian was directing my attention toward it. I didn't know why. There seemed to be just an absence of interesting coral. And then, as I looked, the whole black floor of the valley slowly lifted upward and started gently to waft its way away from us. As it moved, its edges were rippling softly and I could see that underneath it was pure white. I was transfixed by the realisation that what I was looking at was an eight-foot-wide giant manta ray.

It banked away in a wide, sweeping turn in the deeper water. It seemed to be moving breathtakingly slowly, and I was desperate to keep up with it. I came down the side of the reef to follow it. Ian motioned me not to alarm the creature, but just move slowly. I had quickly realised that its size was deceptive and it was moving much more swiftly than I realised. It banked again round the contour of the reef, and I began to see its shape more clearly. It was very roughly diamond-shaped. Its tail is not long, like a sting ray's. The most extraordinary thing is its head. Where you would expect its head to be, it's almost as if something has taken a bite out of it instead. From the two forward points – the outer edges of the 'bite', if you see what I mean – depend two horns, folded downward. And on each of these horns is a single large black eye.

As it moved, shimmering and undulating its giant wings, folding itself through the water, I felt that I was looking at the single most beautiful and unearthly thing I had ever seen in my life. Some people have described them as looking like living stealth bombers, but it is an evil image to apply to a creature so majestic, fluid, and benign.

I followed it as it swam around the outside of the reef. I couldn't follow fast or well, but it was making such wide, sweeping turns that I only had to move relatively short distances round the reef to keep it in sight. Twice, even three times it circled round the reef and then at last it disappeared and I thought I had lost it for good. I stopped and looked around. No. It had definitely gone. I was saddened, but exhilarated with wonder at what I had seen. Then I became aware of a shadow moving on the sea floor at the periphery of my vision. I looked up, unprepared for what I then saw.

The manta ray soared over the top of the reef above me, only this time it had two more in its wake behind it. Together the three vast creatures, moving in perfect, undulating harmony of line, as if following invisible rollercoaster rails, sped off and away till they were lost at last in the darkening distance of the water.

I was very quiet that evening as we packed the Sub Bug back into its big silver box. I thanked Ian for finding the manta rays. I said I understood about not riding them.

'Ah, no worries, mate,' he said. 'No worries at all.'

from *The Salmon of Doubt*
by Douglas Adams

Text 3 – Media text

Mickey was bundled into the back of a car. After several miles, his owner pulled up, opened the door, and flung Mickey out onto the road.

Mickey was just inches away from being crushed to death when he was rescued and taken to safety.

This case is not unusual. Every year people who are bored with their new pets simply throw them away.

This kitten was barely recognisable after avoiding a horrifying death. Some youths tried to drown her in engine oil. We named her Olive.

Remarkably, despite her suffering, Olive made a good recovery, and now has a safe new home. The Inspector who found her says "Olive's story shows the senseless cruelty the Society has to deal with on a daily basis".

Just a small regular gift of £3 a month can help our work to prevent animals suffering cruelty

Whether at local, national or international level, the RSPCA campaigns for improvements in animal welfare.

We are currently concerned with an early phasing out of the battery cage, a ban on hunting with dogs, improved conditions for farm, zoo and circus animals and finding humane alternatives to replace animals in experiments.

Keeping a watchful eye: Alan Pugh an RSPCA Market Inspector. A recent RSPCA survey of animal welfare at livestock markets in England and Wales revealed that many were failing to comply with basic welfare rules.

Members of the public can use the RSPCA's National Cruelty Line to report animals in need of our help.

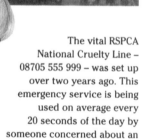

The vital RSPCA National Cruelty Line – 08705 555 999 – was set up over two years ago. This emergency service is being used on average every 20 seconds of the day by someone concerned about an animal in need of our help.

Bill Osment/RSPCA

RSPCA

The RSPCA runs 4 hospitals, 51 animal centres, 39 clinics and a further 19 animal welfare centres in England and Wales. In 1998 an astonishing total of 286,540 treatments were given.

An orphaned baby hare is fed using a syringe in one of the RSPCA's animal hospitals.

RSPCA Inspectors respond quickly to reports of cruelty to animals, acting to prevent ill-treatment. Our 320 RSPCA Inspectors form the largest non-governmental law enforcement agency in the UK – in 1998 investigating 124,374 complaints.

Ken McKay/RSPCA

RSPCA inspectors – the front line against cruelty to animals.

Registered charity no. 219099

The aims of the RSPCA are to prevent cruelty and promote kindness to animals. Your donation will contribute to this important work.

Reading test

You have one hour to complete this test. Answer all of the questions.

The spaces for each answer and the number of marks indicate how much you need to write.

Questions 1–6 are about *A Kestrel for a Knave.*

1 Complete the following table, giving one thing that Billy does with each item.   (1 mark)

Item	What Billy does
scrap of beef	
swivel	
leash	

2 What does the hawk do when it bates? Tick one box.   (1 mark)

Fly away   ❑

Hang upside down from the glove   ❑

Eat a scrap of meat   ❑

Freeze and remain silent   ❑

3 Look at the section 'Billy approached the hawk slowly' to 'tying the end round his little finger'.   (4 marks)

From this section how do you know that Billy knows a lot about how to deal with the hawk?

Give two examples of what he says or does and explain how this shows he is very knowledgeable.

Example: ....

Explanation: ....

....

....

Reading test (cont'd)

Example: ....

Explanation: ....

....

....

4 **Look at the conversation between Billy and the boy on the tricycle.**
Why does the boy 'laugh without smiling'? (2 marks)

....

....

....

....

....

5 **Look at the final paragraph, beginning 'The boy stood up, straddling the tricycle frame'.**
How does the writer create a sense of the boy's fear in this paragraph?

You should write about:

• the way the hawk is described

• the language used to describe the boy's actions. (5 marks)

....

....

....

....

....

....

....

....

....

....

....

....

6 **How does the writer create the sense that Billy is at ease with the wild bird he is training?**

You should write about:

• the way Billy behaves towards the hawk

• the way the hawk responds to Billy

• the difference between the hawk's behaviour with Billy and with the boy on the tricycle. **(6 marks)**

....

....

....

....

....

....

....

....

....

....

....

....

....

....

....

....

....

....

....

....

....

Questions 7–12 are about *The Salmon of Doubt*

7 Look at the paragraph beginning 'I was moving forward slowly'.

How does the writer create a feeling of slow, gentle movement?
Give one example and explain what effect it has.

(2 marks)

Example: ....

....

Explanation: ....

....

8 What does the phrase 'I was transfixed by the realisation' suggest about
how the writer felt about seeing a manta ray?

(2 marks)

....

....

....

....

....

9 Look at the paragraph beginning 'As it moved'. Give two examples from the
paragraph that show how the writer feels about the manta ray and
explain why each is effective.

(2 marks)

Example: ....

....

Explanation: ....

....

....

Example: ....

....

Explanation: ....

....

....

....

10 Look at the section 'No. It had definitely gone' to 'distance of the water'.

Why does the writer feel 'saddened but exhilarated'? (2 marks)

....

....

....

11 How does the writer create a feeling of excitement and surprise in this section? (4 marks)

....

....

....

....

....

....

....

....

12 How successful is the writer in recreating his underwater experience?

You should write about:

• how he sets the scene

• his description of the manta ray

• the way he involves the reader. (5 marks)

....

....

....

....

....

....

....

....

....

Questions 13–16 are about the RSPCA leaflet

13 **What is the purpose of this leaflet? Give two ways to show what the purpose is.** (3 marks)

Purpose:..

....

....

a) ....

....

b) ....

....

14 **a) Why are inverted commas placed around the words 'Olive's story . . . a daily basis'?**

(1 mark)

....

....

....

....

b) What is the effect of including this text? (1 mark)

....

....

....

....

15 **Look at the banner heading. Comment on the use of the words
'just', 'small' and 'prevent animals suffering cruelty' in the heading.** (2 marks)

....

....

....

....

....

....

16 ....

Comment on the overall effectiveness of the layout of the leaflet.

You should write about:

• use of pictures

• font size and style

• general organisation. (5 marks)

....

....

....

....

....

....

....

....

....

....

....

....

....

....

....

....

....

....

....

....

Section A

You have 45 minutes to complete this test.

You should spend 15 minutes planning your answer.

Complete your plan in the space below. Write your answer on a separate sheet of paper.

This task is worth 30 marks. You will be awarded marks for:

• sentence structure and punctuation	(8 marks)
• text structure and organisation	(8 marks)
• composition and effect.	(14 marks)

Imagine that you do some volunteer work for a local animal sanctuary which takes in stray and neglected pets as well as caring for injured wild animals and birds. The animal sanctuary will have to close in three months' time unless extra funding can be raised.

Write a letter to your local council to persuade them to give a grant to the animal sanctuary.

Make your writing as persuasive as possible but remember it is a formal letter.

Planning sheet

Make brief notes under the following headings:

Services provided by the animal sanctuary

....

....

What the money is needed for

....

....

Benefits to the council and local community

....

....

Word bank

List any persuasive/emotive words or phrases you might use in your letter.

....

....

Section B

You have 30 minutes to complete this test.

You should spend 5–10 minutes planning your writing.

Complete your plan in the space below. Write your answer on a separate sheet of paper.

This task is worth 20 marks. You will be awarded marks for:

- sentence structure/punctuation and text organisation   (6 marks)
- composition and effect   (10 marks)
- spelling.   (4 marks)

You have been asked to write a contribution for the school magazine about your ambitions and plans for the future.

Write a short article in which you explain what your ambition is, how you hope to achieve it and how you would feel if you were able to do this.

Planning sheet

Make brief notes under the following headings:

Ambition

....

....

....

....

How to achieve ambition

....

....

....

....

Feelings

....

....

....

....

Paper 3: Shakespeare (reading & understanding)

The set Shakespeare texts for SATs are:

Much Ado About Nothing	**Pages 52–59**
Richard III	**Pages 60–67**
The Tempest	**Pages 68–75**

Answer the question about the Shakespeare play you have studied or the general question that best fits your set scenes.

1 *Much Ado About Nothing*: Act III Scene 2 lines 59–end and Act IV Scene 1 lines 1–105

In these scenes Claudio believes Don John's lies about Hero and sets out to disgrace her because he believes she has been unfaithful to him.

How does Shakespeare develop Claudio's lack of trust in Hero during these scenes?

....

....

....

....

2 *Richard III*: Act I Scene 1 lines 1–122 and Act II Scene 1 lines 47–end

Richard III is considered to be one of Shakespeare's most villainous characters. He always thinks about how he can destroy the lives of others to improve his own.

In these scenes, how does Shakespeare present Richard as a villain who manipulates other people?

....

....

....

....

3 *The Tempest*: Act II Scene 2 lines 1–101 and Act III Scene 2 lines 1–79

In the play Caliban exchanges one cruel master, Prospero, for a drunken one, Stephano. He seems happy to be treated badly by Stephano.

How does Shakespeare present the relationship between Stephano, Trinculo and Caliban in these scenes?

....

....

....

....

General questions

Answer the question that best fits the specific scenes you have studied.

1 Compare the behaviour of the main character in each of the two extracts.

....
....
....
....

2 How do characters respond to the pressure they are under in these scenes?

....
....
....
....

3 What changes occur in the relationships presented in these scenes?

....
....
....
....

4 How would you direct these scenes to create an appropriate atmosphere?
Give direction about how characters should behave and the way their lines should be spoken.

....
....
....
....
....
....
....
....